SALLY

S0-ACA-572

A Plan for
Measuring the
Performance of
Social Programs

LABOR ECONOMICS AND URBAN STUDIES

Previously published in this series:

PRAEGER SPECIAL STUDIES IN
U.S. ECONOMIC AND SOCIAL DEVELOPMENT

A Plan for Measuring the Performance of Social Programs

THE APPLICATION OF OPERATIONS RESEARCH METHODOLOGY

David S. Alberts

Foreword by
Oscar A. Ornati

PRAEGER PUBLISHERS
New York • Washington • London

The purpose of Praeger Special Studies is to make specialized research in U.S. and international economics and politics available to the academic, business, and government communities. For further information, write to the Special Projects Division, Praeger Publishers, Inc., 111 Fourth Avenue, New York, N.Y. 10003.

PRAEGER PUBLISHERS
111 Fourth Avenue, New York, N.Y. 10003, U.S.A.
5, Cromwell Place, London S.W.7, England

Published in the United States of America in 1970
by Praeger Publishers, Inc.

All rights reserved

© 1970 by Praeger Publishers, Inc.

Library of Congress Catalog Card Number: 72-117480

Printed in the United States of America

FOREWORD
by Oscar A. Ornati

The 1960's witnessed, in the United States, a
major change in sociopolitical expectation: in the
refusal to tolerate inequality, poverty, the meanness
of life. Caused by and influencing a set of political and intellectual developments occurring around
the beginning of the decade--the struggle for civil
rights, the election of President Kennedy, the success of Michael Harrington's book on poverty, The
Other America, the activities of the President's Committee on Juvenile Delinquency, the "Gray Areas Program" of the Ford Foundation--the new attitude led to
an extraordinary increase of governmental activities
and spending in the area of social welfare.

Under the banner of the War on Poverty, the Office of Economic Opportunitiy (OEO), the Department
of Labor, and the Department of Health, Education and
Welfare (HEW) spearheaded the federal thrust to establish anti-poverty, manpower, health, housing, education, and other action projects. Such programs
spread throughout the nation with a speed that made
it almost impossible to keep a current inventory, to
say nothing of appraising them as projects or evaluating their programmatic impact. The shift in resource allocation that has occurred is partly visible
in aggregate statistics, such as the increased proportion of the gross national product attributable to
health and education. But the impact of this shift,
whether the new pattern of resource allocation is
either more equitable or more efficient, is something
we know little about.

In the Thirties, when a similar increase in
social welfare activities got underway with the New
Deal, the behavioral sciences remained fundamentally
uninvolved. In fact, they were indirect recipients

of program assistance; and the relatively large
rosters of clerical workers in some of the New Deal
agencies kept "counts" of program activities that
could have made it possible to carry out research of
dimensions never before thought possible. Yet little
research on New Deal programs was in fact conducted,
and we still know little about the effectiveness of
programs undertaken by the Works Projects Administration (WPA) or by the Civilian Conservation Corps
(CCC). The opposite situation characterizes the
Sixties: OEO's enabling legislation specifically
earmarked as much as 15 percent of total funds for
evaluation research. The demand for evaluation of
non-OEO programming increased also, as, following
the example of the Controller's Office in the Department of Defense, the Bureau of the Budget and President Johnson ordered all of the federal executive
agencies to initiate program planning and budgeting
systems. Thus, since 1965 there has been a flowering
of evaluation research as social scientists joined
federal and state agencies and as universities and
private research firms contracted to provide the new
evaluative services.

Evaluation research was of course not invented
in the Sixties, and its development has not been en-
tirely a matter of responding to the needs of bureau-
crats and legislators concerned with the impact of
the expenditure of public funds. Antecedents of
evaluation research can be found in the practice of
private planning and, indeed, in the attempts of any
entrepreneur to calculate whether an investment will
pay off. More direct antecedents of evaluation research can be found in the intellectual debates of
the Thirties on the very possibility of planning and
in the debates on the usefulness of socialist planning as against the market mechanism. Indeed, O.
Lange's essays on the function of the central planning board in the socialist state in the Review of
Economic Studies of 1936 and 1937 showed beyond possible challenge how the allocation of public services
could rationally be established without reference to
private market mechanism, thereby establishing an
approach which simultaneously evaluates and acts upon
allocative decisions.[1] A more direct precursor of

evaluation research activities can be found in the project appraisals prepared in connection with international loans and grants for the building of railways, harbors, dams, and roads in underdeveloped countries. The World Bank, forced to do so by its Articles of Agreement, probably contributed most to the development of project appraisal technique and methodology.

In spite of such illustrious antecedents, program evaluation has so far contributed little and has affected few policy decisions. Professor Rossi, a sociologist from the University of Chicago, reporting in On Fighting Poverty on studies involving over 1,100 evaluation research projects, notes that "the flowering has meant more the encouragement of weeds than of more desirable species" and that "much evaluation can be called research only by the most charitable extension of the meaning of the term."[2] Nor is Rossi's criticism applicable only to the specifically contracted evaluations of limited antipoverty or manpower training programs structured to influence a marginal social problem--in many ways a more arduous endeavor than assessing the impact of governmental action on central social conditions. Our ability to evaluate major established governmental agencies is equally limited. A recent, thorough, and scholarly evaluation of the U.S. Employment Service by Leonard Adams of Cornell cannot tell us whether funds allocated for that program are effective or not.[3] Recently Science carried a hot debate among leading demographers as to whether governmental outlays making contraceptive services available to the public were having an impact on birth rates.[4]

This is not the place to discuss at length the reason for the current dearth of effective program evaluations. Lack of data, the lack of controlled experiments, the "politics" of agencies and research contractors, and the great number of poorly designed experiments are the more generally recognized problems. More sophisticated analyses point to the inherently "weak" effects of current programs; in the field of morbidity and mortality, e.g., it can be argued that the introduction of modern medicine and public sanitation produced dramatic results and that thereafter, new gains in the reduction of morbidity and mortality--through neighborhood health centers-- can at best be small and difficult to trace. Probably central is the lack of a broad and flexible general methodology.

The lack of an effective methodology is accepted, albeit implicitly, evey by scholars and practitioners who rate present achievements in evaluation research higher than I do and credit it with greater influence upon policy. Thus, Dr. R. A. Levine, the former Chief of Evaluation of OEO, begins an essentially positive report with the statement "Policy evaluation is an art . . . ,"[5] and Rossi reminds us of the need to link "social placebos" to evaluation reserach. At the heart of the problem of methodology is the fact that criteria, techniques, and measures of evaluation are called for at many levels, not all of which are rec- ognized as part of the process of program evaluation. Recognized are, first, the need to evaluate a broad governmental thrust, e.g., the War on Poverty, in terms of a reduction in the number of the poor. Sec- ond, criteria and measurements for the evaluation of individual programs, e.g., Head Start, are needed. Third, criteria are needed for comparing the effects of individual programs against one another, e.g., Head Start vs. Planned Parenthood centers. What often is not recognized as integral and necessary is the need to evaluate the very broad governmental pro- gram, e.g., the War on Poverty, and that it must be evaluated in relationship to alternative broad gov- ernmental programs, e.g., the need to improve urban life.

Dr. Alberts claims both that this can be done and that the appropriate methodology has its basis in operations research. The claim is valid, since oper- ations reserach provides, in the words of Ackoff and Sasieni in Fundamentals of Operations Research, "a systematic and rational approach to the fundamental problem involved in the control of systems by making decisions which, in some sense, achieve the best re- sults in light of all the information that is profit- able for use."

The reader should not be put off either by the inclusiveness of the definition or by the fact that so far operations research has been applied mostly to the solution of trite problems. When all is said and done, evaluation research deals with planning; and operations research, by forcing the correct formulation of goals and objectives, deals with the essential properties of planning. First, planning is anticipatory decision making; second, it involves interdependent decisions (we need not here stumble over the faddist use of the term "system"); third, planning takes place in dynamic contexts; and fourth, it calls for being aware that the consequences of doing nothing are more likely than not to be undesirable.

Thus, this work is "at the frontiers." It is at the frontier of operations research, of program evaluation, and of planned social change. It surely will not usher in the millennium, but it deserves serious consideration and much experimentation with the methodology it suggests.

NOTES

1. Oscar Lange, "The Function of the Control Planning Board in the Socialist State" in The Review of Economic Studies, March 1936.

2. P. H. Rossi, "Practice, Method, and Theory in Evaluating Social-Action Programs" in On Fighting Poverty, ed. J. L. Sundquist (New York: Basic Books, 1969), p. 218.

3. L. P. Adams, The Public Employment in Transition, 1933-1968 (Ithaca, New York: New York State School of Industrial and Labor Relations, Cornell University, 1969).

4. Science, June and September 1969.

5. R. A. Levine, "Evaluating the War on Poverty" in On Fighting Poverty, ed. J. L. Sundquist (New York: Basic Books, 1969), pp. 188-216.

ACKNOWLEDGMENTS

This book could not have been written were it not for the efforts of several people. The development of this work from roughly formulated theory and research plans was aided immeasurably by the suggestions and criticisms of Dr. Richard C. Clelland.

The data used, along with many studied comments and suggestions, were graciously supplied by Dr. Julius Jahn.

I should also like to thank Drs. David Conrath, William Gomberg, and Richard Swersey, whose reactions were extremely helpful. Thanks are due also to Elizabeth Adamson for her untiring efforts at transcribing and typing the early drafts of this work.

Funds provided by the Management Science Center of the University of Pennsylvania enabled me to devote my full-time efforts to this book in its developmental stage.

Finally, I wish to express my appreciation to my wife, Mimi, whose encouragement and devotion enabled me to complete this book.

CONTENTS

LIST OF TABLES

LIST OF FIGURES

FIGURES IN THE APPENDIXES

A Plan for
Measuring the
Performance of
Social Programs

CHAPTER **1** INTRODUCTION

PURPOSE OF THE STUDY

We are presently in the midst of a significant
expansion of social programs, both in number and in
the total amount of resources applied to them. In
1960 domestic governmental programs numbered less
than 50, while in 1968 the number of programs exceeded 400. What is most disturbing is that there is no
overall methodology which can be used to tell us how
effective each program is in relation to the achievement of social goals. Lacking such a procedure, the
efficient and effective allocation of our society's
resources becomes very difficult indeed. In addition to the proliferation of programs, we are witness-
es to increasing rates of technological change which
threaten us with having our "best" solutions becoming
obsolete before they are implemented. Taken together,
these facts highlight the necessity of having a methodology capable of producing measures of performance
or effectiveness for social programs concerned with
education, job training, health, or any of the various other aspects of societal concern.

In practice the word "program" usually refers
to an activity concerned with quite specific objectives. I should like the definition to include any
possible action of a society at any level of government. Thus, we will be dealing with programs which
may contain other "programs." The methodology presented in this book should enable one to derive a
measure of the performance of a program, regardless
of its position in a hierarchial structure. The measure of performance will reflect a general statement
concerning the goals of the society. (See Chapters
3 and 4 for delineation of individual and societal

3

goals.) This statement will be made but once; that
is, all individual measures of performance for programs will essentially be derived from a single statement of social goals. For example, one of society's
goals may be to provide an environment in which every
individual has an equal chance--regardless of race,
creed, or income--of receiving an education commensu-
rate with his ability. It is assumed that this goal
will be rather stable over at least the short run.
Consider three "programs" for which one wishes to
obtain a measure of performance. The first is the
activities of the Department of Health, Education
and Welfare (HEW); the second, the activities of the
Board of Education of New York City; and the third, a
program in remedial reading in Public School 63. All
of the derived measures will stem from the statement
of the above goal of society. The difference between
the actual measures will be a function of their respective scopes. Naturally, the measure derived for
the remedial reading program will reflect mainly that
contribution to the probability of success in an individual's quest for education which can be attributed
to improved reading ability. The measure derived for
the Board of Education will be much broader in scope,
including the effect of the individual's preparation
through high school. The evaluation of HEW approaches the evaluation of our society's realization of its
goal with respect to educational opportunity, but
does not reach it. This is because there are other
activities performed by organizations other than HEW
that contribute to the realization of this societal
goal. It should be noted that although the first two
are not normally considered to be programs in the or-
dinary sense of the word, they can be evaluated in
this manner. Naturally, as one tackles programs higher up in the structure--that is, programs which en-
compass more aspects of the problem and/or more of
the population--the complexity of the derived measure
of performance will increase. It may be desirable to
build measures of performance of programs by first
determining measures of the programs which they encom-
pass.

Thus, the methodology will be considerably more
general in its application than it would have been if

it provided measures of performance without using a
statement of societal goals as a basis. The application of this methodology can be made at any level
of the program structure. This makes possible two
types of comparisons. First, programs at different
levels, say at municipal and state levels, can be
compared with respect to their relative contributions
to societal goals. This type of comparison is extremely important, as it may provide us with a more
realistic way of allocating resources among levels
of government. The second kind of comparison is
among various alternative programs at a given level
of complexity. This will be of use in an inter-
organization allocation of funds.

SCOPE OF THE STUDY

As stated above, the purpose of this book is to
provide a framework in which the performance of a
social action can be measured.

Social actions are viewed from two different
perspectives. One perspective is that of the individuals directly affected by or participating in a
social action or activity; the other view is that of
the society at large. Another way to think of these
two viewpoints is to associate one with the individual in society and the other with society at large.
Each viewpoint can be taken as a basis for the development of a measure of performance of social services. The methods by which these alternative viewpoints lead to operational criteria, and thus to the
evaluation of alternative programs or actions, form
the body of this book.

Each viewpoint starts our investigation with a
different set of goals and objectives.

Implications of Alternative Sets of Goals

The goals of social programs are a reflection
of the goals of society. Therefore the goals of society per se were investigated for the purposes of
this book.

The relationship between the individual and society is unquestionably symbiotic; nevertheless,
differences of opinion exist as to the degree of re-
sponsibility and authority to be enjoyed by each man.
Kant felt that the individual should be regarded as
an end unto himself,[1] while Hegel contended that the
individual exists for the sake of the state.[2] Although both these statements are oversimplifications,
they serve as expressions of the two basic schools
of thought on the relationship between society and
the individual. Carried to extreme, in political
terms these positions would be called anarchy and
dictatorship.

If the sovereignty of the individual is held
paramount, then the goals of society are the goals
of its individual members. If that of the state is
held supreme, then the goals of society are the goals
of the state.

I will develop an expression for the goal(s) of
the individual as well as a measure of the degree to
which these goals are realized. An individual's goal
is taken to be the maximization of the value to him
of the environment he is in. This environment is
expressed as a function of his various needs for objects, tangible and intangible, and the degree to
which each of his needs is satisfied. Then I will
develop a theoretical formulation of the goals of society and obtain a method for evaluating the success
of a particular social program in terms of these
goals.

Once the two statements of goals have been presented, the way will be clear to take the steps
necessary to facilitate the use of each set of goals
in the evaluation of social actions. Two such steps
remain. First, measures of the realization of each
set of goals must be constructed in order to provide
a yardstick of success. The completion of this step
will result in an ideal procedure or methodology for
evaluating programs. However, such a procedure would
be far too costly to use. Thus, the second step is
to develop approximations to the measures developed,
which will make it possible to employ the methodology.

I will summarize briefly the approach to be taken in constructing measures of the degree to which each set of goals is realized and the approximations to these measures.

Measures of Goal Realization and Development
of Approximations to the Measures

In order that a formulation of goals may become useful or operational, a measure of the degree to which they are being realized must be provided. Such measures will be developed for both individual and societal goals in Chapters 3 and 4, respectively. In the case of individual goals, experimental procedures for determining both the objects for which an individual has a need and the relative value of these objects to the individual will be presented. A quite general set of societal goals will be established, as well as measures of the degree of realization of these goals as they relate to specific social programs. Thus, these quantities will measure how close a particular program comes to the attainment of its goals.

The acquisition of the data needed for the computation of these ideal measures is costly and difficult. Sampling techniques can be used to reduce cost to some extent; but to make the theory really usable, approximations are needed. In Chapter 5 two kinds of approximations are developed. The first kind involves estimating the value of the measure by simplifying the operational procedure. This method will be introduced in approximating the degree to which individual goals are satisfied. It involves introduction of a standard object set, which eliminates the need to run the experiments outlined to ascertain the objects that each individual needs.

The second kind of approximation involves measuring or estimating an indicator of a measure rather than estimating or measuring the measure itself. This method will be developed for societal goals. Instead of attempting to deal directly with the goals of society, the ways in which a society attempts to approach its goals are examined. A measure of the

success which society has in performing its functions
is used as an indicant of the success which society
has in realizing its goals.

The approximations that are presented pertain
to a specific application of the methodology, to
which I will now turn my attention.

APPLICATION OF THE METHODOLOGY TO EVALUATION OF SOCIAL PROGRAMS

The final portion of this book consists of a
presentation of the application of the methods developed.

The School of Social Work of the University of
Pennsylvania has performed some of the most complete
data-gathering experiments in the field of social
welfare. Three-hour interviews were held with both
present and past recipients of selected welfare programs and non-recipients with similar demographic
profiles. These interviews provided us with sufficient data to employ the approximate measures developed in Chapter 5. The details of the application
of these procedures to the actual programs can be
found in Chapter 6, along with comparisons based upon the approximate measures.

NOTES

1. I. Kant, "Foundations of the Metaphysics
of Morals," Critique of Practical Reason and Other
Writings in Moral Philosophy (Chicago: University
of Chicago Press, 1949), p. 86.

2. G. Hegel, Philosophy of Right   (Oxford:
Clarendon Press, 1942), p. 156.

CHAPTER **2** STATE OF THE ART

INTRODUCTION

The problem of evaluating a given social program and the problem of measuring or evaluating the
effectiveness of society (or its representative, government) differ, in my opinion, only by a scale factor. The "evaluation" of society, as well as of
programs or actions of society, can be traced back
centuries before the birth of Christ. Historically,
this evaluation, including the selection of the criterion or objective function, has been largely the
province of the philosopher.

With the advent of "science" in the 18th century a further development occurred. Scientists began to take an interest in the problem of evaluation.
They tended to accept general statements of the objective function from philosophers, and then they
attempted to "operationalize" the concepts embodied
in these statements. The philosophical concepts developed over the centuries for evaluating society
have been used both implicitly and explicitly by
those attempting to measure the effectiveness of its
programs. Three bodies of knowledge dealing specifically with the measurement of the effectiveness of
social activities have emerged. They are social
(economic) accounting, welfare economics, and social
work. Before discussing the relevant state of the
art in each of these three areas, a review of some of
the philosophical foundations upon which a measure of
performance for society might be based will be given.

PHILOSOPHICAL FOUNDATIONS OF SOCIAL CRITERIA

Any method of evaluating a society's effectiveness must be based upon a consistent set of concepts

9

as to what the relationship between the individual
and society ought to be, at least as far as the goals
of each are concerned.

Put in the simplest terms, the two main points
of view advanced by philosophers concerning this relationship are (a) the individual exists to serve society and (b) society exists to serve the individual.

In a sense, the first view was expressed by Plato
in his Republic, a utopia where the good of the whole,
rather than the happiness of its citizens, has prece-
dence.[1] The second view, that society exists to serve
the individual, was held by I. Kant, among others.

If one accepts the first point of view, what
sort of statement of a criterion of societal action
and evaluation procedure does this imply? If one accepts the second? In the first case the goals of society are formulated without any consideration of the
goals of the individual members. This being the case,
all that would matter would be an aggregate value of
some chosen measure of performance; the actual distribution or dispersion of this measure would be irrele-
vant. In the second case, however, a conflict arises
which makes an evaluation difficult except in very unusual circumstances. When two individuals' interests
clash, who shall give way? Only under the unlikely
circumstance that an alternative is best for all individuals simultaneously is this difficulty completely
eliminated. Welfare economics has attempted to deal
with this problem, and I will discuss these attempts
in a later section.

First, I will consider some writings which deal
with the relationship between the individual and the
state, followed by a discussion of some dealing with
the goals of society.

Various Views of the Individual-State Relationship

The view of the relationship between the individual and the state has undergone a steady evolution
from ancient to modern times. This evolution, with

minor exceptions, has brought more "rights" to more
individuals as history has unfolded. Put another
way, the professed goals of society and those of the
individual have tended over time to agree more and
more closely. The following discussion of philosophical thought is not intended to be complete in any
way, but rather to show the reader where he can find
the origin and criticism of various ideas which appear later in this thesis in the formulation of the
methodology needed for the evaluation of social services.

    The two conflicting views presented previously--
that society exists to serve the individual and that
the individual exists to serve society--have rarely
existed in philosophical writings in an unqualified
or unconditional state. It is more accurate to think
of the possible relationships between the individual
and society as forming a continuum with complete authority on one and and complete liberty on the other.
To illustrate this point I would like to quote from a
letter which T. Hobbes wrote to F. Godolphin as an
introduction to his Leviathan:

          I know not how the world will receive
          it, nor how it may reflect on those
          that shall favour it. For in a way be-
          set with those that contend, on one
          side for too great liberty, and on the
          other side for too much authority, 'tis
          hard to pass between the points of both
          unwounded.[2]

    Hobbes is generally considered royalist in the
extreme. He contends that men are ruled by the im-
pulse to self-preservation and, without government,
would destroy each other. Men can escape from this
situation only by combining into communities and sub-
jecting themselves to a central authority. This pact
or covenant is not between the citizens and the rulers
(as in J. J. Rousseau and J. Locke) but among all citizens; and once a ruling body is chosen, no more discussion is warranted and no rebellion is justified.
This implies that the goals of the majority (those
who selected the ruling body) might influence the

ruling body initially, but that the goals of society
would soon be exclusively those of the ruling body.

When we turn to the writings of Locke, we en-
counter a different point of view. Locke contends
that self-interest and the general interest coincide
only in the long run, and that government is a con-
tract binding only upon individuals who have consent-
ed. But, as he explains: "But though this be a
state of liberty, yet it is not a state of license;
though man in that state has an uncontrollable liberty to dispose of his person or possessions, yet he
has not liberty to destroy himself, or so much as any
creature in his possession. . . ."[3] This seems to
imply that a societal criterion could be derived by
using some individualistic criterion subject to a
number of constraints.

Many other philosophers have expressed views on
the extent of liberty the individual should possess.
G. Hegel and J. P. Sartre, for example, hold conflict-
ing positions. Hegel expresses in his Philosophy of
Right the idea that the moral fulfillment of the individual can occur only when he is a member of the
state, while Sartre contends that man is not merely
free, but is freedom and can have existence only if
he has freedom of choice.

Thus, Western social philosophers have differed
greatly on the degree of authority that is vested in
the state. Those philosophers who emphasize individual goals seem careful to point out the need for re-
solving conflicts of interest. On the other hand,
those who adopt the opposite position feel that the
ultimate goal for the individual is realizable only
through the state. Both a societal objective function
and an individualistic objective function may reason-
ably be derived from the several branches of philosophy. Thus I have elected to develop both types of
function in this book. I would like first to discuss
my conception of the goals and objectives of society,
which will form the basis for the development of a
societal objective function.

Societal Goals as a Basis for an
Objective Function

The goals and objectives of a community can be thought of as either a function of the individual goals and objectives of the members or as attributes of the community as a whole. If the first belief is held, then both a search for individual goals and a search for an aggregation rule to combine them must be undertaken. In the second case, a search for community or societal goals must be made. One type of societal goal is called a universal goal, a goal which is agreed upon by all reasonable men.

The search for universal goals has been a favorite preoccupation of philosophers. Until the 18th century the three ideals of man were identified as truth, beauty, and good.[4] Modern philosophers identified a fourth--plenty or abundance. Could there not be just one universal ideal of man? In a sense, a meta-ideal was sought. This was identified by E. A. Singer when he observed that implicit in every want or desire of man is the power of attainment.[5] Put another way, the means to ends are desired simultaneously with the ends themselves. For some, this may kindle memories of the long-debated question of ends justifying means. I contend that (it follows from Singer's observation) the means to any end are in this sense indivisible from that end. To deny this contention is to argue that one can desire ends without desiring the means of attaining them. The implications of this reasoning are that societal goals can and should be expressed not by merely naming the objective but by including with this statement a plan for its attainment. A societal objective function based upon this viewpoint will be developed in Chapter 4.

THE DEVELOPMENT OF THREE DISCIPLINES CONCERNED
WITH SOCIETAL EVALUATION

As mentioned earlier, three distinct disciplines have developed which consider various aspects of

societal performance. Two of these--social accounting and welfare economics--are essentially concerned
with developing general indicators of societal performance, while the other--social work--is concerned
with the design and performance of social programs
aimed at improving the lot of its participants. This
book will attempt to fuse the general nature of the
evaluative aspects of social accounting and welfare
economics with the specific concern of social work
for programs, form a general procedure for evaluating
any type of social service.

    In order to enable the reader to consider the
proposals contained in this book in the context of
current work in related fields, a brief review of
work in each of the above disciplines will be given.
Social accounting and welfare economics will be reviewed first, followed by a discussion of current
technology in social work research.

              Social Accounting and Welfare Economics

    The development of social accounting has until
recently been embedded within the framework of macro-
economics. Like all accounting procedures, it serves
two main functions: it describes the state of the
organization, and it provides a method of using this
description for evaluative purposes. Without such a
system regular observations about the condition of
society could not be made, and decisions about governmental actions (e.g., changing policy on bank re-
serves, poverty programs, reductions in taxes, etc.)
would be made in a state of virtual ignorance.

    Social accounting is a logical outgrowth of na-
tional economic accounting. The origins of such a
system date back to the Political Arithmatick of W.
Petty (1623-87) and the Tableau Economique of F.
Quesnay (1694-1774).[6] The idea of preparing tables
of statistics to give an overview of a nation's
economy was first developed by the classical economists and was later expanded by A. Marshall (1842-
1924) and J. M. Keynes (1883-1946). During periods
of depression and strain a tremendous effort was made
to obtain such data to use as a tool in planning the

economy. The essence of national economic accounting
is that it provides a double look at the economic
state of the nation. Total output of goods and services (gross national product) is broken down by type
of expenditure and product. Further, the distribution
of national income (a debit on one person's book is
a credit on another's) is broken down by sector of
origin and type of income. Progress in this type of
accounting depends upon adopting more precisely defined measures and improving data-collecting procedures. Currently, O. Morgenstern points out, large
errors exist because of inadequate basic data, fitting
of data to concepts, and interpolation to fill gaps.[7]

Instead of asking how relevant the measures are
or how well they reflect the changes which occur, the
trend at the moment is to use more and more sophisticated techniques to reduce error. This seems, however, to be only an attempt to get a more precise
answer to the wrong question or an accurate measure
of the wrong quantity, because it is clear that economic measures alone cannot provide an adequate measure for societal performance. Efforts in this
direction tend toward emphasizing quantitative data
while giving less attention to ideas that are difficult to quantify. A broadening of the concept of
national economic accounting is needed, and initial
efforts along these lines have been made by H.
Schultz and J. W. Kendrick.[8] Kendrick has proposed
to extend the concept of investment to include two
forms of "hidden investment" traditionally overlooked.
One is the investment in human resources, including
health and educational outlays, normally considered
as consumption. The other is industrial investment
in research and development, training, and improved
methods. Schultz has also advocated the inclusion
of investments in human resources, adding migration
to employment opportunities.

These are essentially efforts to patch up an
antiquated method of social accounting. What must
be realized is that the time has come for a complete
overhaul, one which has measures that reflect the
attainment of the goals of society. This presupposes
that the goals of society have been formulated and

that the chosen indicators have been shown to be at least significantly correlated with measures of the attainment of these goals. The past development of national economic accounting has given us a good basis for future efforts by providing reasonable data from which to work.

An attempt at identifying national goals and their indicators has been made by A. D. Biderman.[9] They were derived from statements of national advisory commissions, such as the one appointed by President Hoover and the one appointed by President Eisenhower.[10] State of the Union addresses were also used as sources of indicators.

In reviewing the accomplishments of welfare economics, I found it useful to keep several things in mind. The most important aspect of welfare economics is that it is based upon a consideration of scarce resources and their distribution among the population by means of a free market mechanism, or competition. It should be noted that as time passes, particularly in affluent societies like ours, the range of products and services will steadily increase. Further, the free market mechanism has never been a reality; and the trend seems to be toward less free markets, especially in such essential services as transportation, health, and education.

The following problem is a good example of a situation with which welfare economics may find it difficult to deal. Consider a group of individuals forming a population. An increase of total wealth would generally be considered desirable, but this does not have to be the case. Suppose further that the increase in wealth occurred without any individual in the group having any wealth taken away from him. Again, one would tend to speak of this group as being better off. Again, this would not necessarily be the case. The very fact that some individuals in the group are now better off makes it likely that others perceive themselves as being worse off. "Perceive" is the key word, because it casts this situation out of the traditional realm of economics and into the broad spectrum of the social sciences.

Keeping these points in mind will, I think, more
clearly delineate the accomplishments and problems
of welfare economics.

Welfare economics is concerned with the economic
well-being of individuals or communities. An individual's well-being is greatly affected by the things
he produces and consumes, and thus has a strong economic aspect. "Well-being" has been taken by the
utilitarian economists to mean "happiness" for the
individual and "the sum total of the happiness of all
the individuals" for the community. Utilitarianism
began with the writings of J. Bentham and culminated
in those of J. S. Mill. Bentham popularized the concept of the "greatest good for the greatest number,"
and Mill expanded upon this thought when he wrote:

> The utilitarian morality does recognize
> in human beings the power of sacrificing
> their own greatest good for the good of
> others. It only refuses to admit that
> the sacrifice is itself a good. A sacri-
> fice which does not increase, or tend to
> increase, the sum total of happiness, it
> considers wasted.[11]

Clearly, these statements lead to the conclusion
that the state will have reached an optimal operating
point when the marginal utilities of all men are
equal. Utility was considered to be a property of
objects which creates satisfaction, and happiness
was considered to be the sum of satisfactions. Hence,
to maximize happiness, one should maximize utility.

Utilitarianism, as a theory of ethics, had fall-
en into ill repute by the time that welfare economics,
based upon utility theory, was expounded exhaustively
by A. C. Pigou in 1920.[12] Pigou considered welfare
economics a science because satisfactions were measurable; however, following G. E. Moore, he considered that "good" and "welfare" were unanalyzable.[13] An
essential feature of the Pigovian type of welfare
economics is the assumption that each individual is
a "rational" or "economic" man (i.e., one who tries
to maximize his own satisfaction). As Pigou says:

> It is fair to suppose that most com-
> modities, especially those of wide con-
> sumption that are required, as articles
> of food and clothing are, for direct
> personal use, will be wanted as a means
> to satisfaction, and will, consequently,
> be desired with intensities proportioned
> to the satisfactions they are expected
> to yield.[14]

Marshallian economics of demand used this assumption
to arrive at "optimum" conditions of production and
exchange. It follows from the assumptions of utilitarian economics that the necessary condition for
achieving maximum happiness is that the marginal utility of money must yield the same amount of satisfac-
to everyone. Some discussion as to whether the
marginal utility of money diminishes as real income
increases or as money income increases can be found
in I. M. D. Little's book on welfare economics.[15]
Bentham and Pigou take the first position and Marshall
the second.

    Two main objections to this approach have been
raised:

    1.   Satisfactions cannot be added; therefore,
          it is meaningless to speak of the happi-
          ness of the community as the sum of the
          happiness of individuals, and the happi-
          ness of individuals as the sum of their
          satisfactions.

    2.   The satisfactions and happiness of dif-
          ferent people cannot be compared satis-
          factorily.

The second criticism has meant that scholars have
either thrown up their hands in despair at this point
or have been forced to seek more acceptable methods
of comparison. The first criticism, however, has
been more telling; it has led to the general acceptance of a theory based upon the view that only an
ordinal system may be applied to satisfaction. As
a result of abandoning the additivy of satisfactions,

indifference curve analysis has replaced Marshallian
analysis, the former being cardinal while the latter
is ordinal. Little renamed indifference curves
"behavior lines" and outlined an operational procedure for obtaining them.[16] A point on a higher behavior line is considered to be a "chosen position,"
i.e., one that is selected or preferred; but this
does not imply anything about the amount of satisfaction present. This translation of utility theory
into choice theory has been called the "theory of
revealed preference."[17] It shows how the consumer's
"behavior map" can be constructed from his purchases.

Behavior maps, while not considered applicable
to individuals with changing tastes, can be applied
if behavior can be said to be consistent. The evaluation of the appropriateness of the statement "being
on a higher behavior line" as an indication of ex-
periencing an increase in welfare involves several
considerations, the most important of which are (1)
length of time involved, (2) effect of other individuals, (3) changes in taste or social position, (4)
stability of behavior.[18] Even if one accepts the
idea that moving to a higher behavior line implies
an increase in welfare, the problem of relating this
to the general welfare remains. This school of economic thought, by its rejection of additive satisfaction, has also rejected Bentham's principle of the
greatest good for the greatest number, which implies
that the sum of the measures of individuals' welfare
is equal to a measure of the general welfare. Two
methods have been developed to replace the summing
of individual utilities, with the objective of making
comparisons between pairs of situations. The first
method requires only that when some people have moved
to a higher behavior line and the rest have remained
unchanged, the resulting situation can be considered
better than the initial one. Clearly, a community in
which one can find an action that has no adverse effect upon anybody is quite unusual in its makeup;
but it may be desirable for some purposes to work with
such a formulation.

The second view can be called the "compensation
principle." It was enunciated by N. Kaldor when he

wrote:

> In all cases, therefore, where a certain
> policy leads to an increase in physical
> productivity, and thus of aggregate real
> income, the economist's case for the pol-
> icy is quite unaffected by the compara-
> bility of individual satisfactions; since
> in all such cases it is possible to make
> everybody better off than before, or at
> any rate to make some people better off
> without making anybody worse off. . . .
> In order to establish this case, it is
> quite sufficient for him to show that
> even if all those who suffer as a result
> are fully compensated for their loss, the
> rest of the community will still be better
> off than before.[19]

The above criterion, known as the compensation
criterion, has been attacked by W. J. Baumol for not
taking income distribution into account (i.e., for
ignoring the differences among individual incomes).[20]
J. R. Hicks endorsed Kaldor and even went so far as
to state, "If A is made so much better off by the
change that he could compensate B for his loss, and
still have something left over, then the reorganiza-
tion is an unequivocal improvement."[21]

Besides the criticism raised by Baumol, some
practical difficulties in the application of this
criterion have been mentioned in the literature. If
one is to compensate those who have lost, one needs
to know exactly how much they have lost in some consistent unit of measurement, say utiles, which in
turn entails knowing their behavior map. In order
to make sure that there are enough excess utiles to
assure that at least someone is "better off" after
the losers are compensated, one needs to know the
gainers' maps as well. Clearly, it is rather difficult to run the experiments necessary to know everyone's maps. Returning to the criticism raised by
Baumol, one might ask whether B was "happy" to be
compensated by A or whether such compensation actually lowered B's happiness or welfare. T. Scitovsky's

criticism of the compensation principle was that if
compensation was theoretical and not actual, different distributions of real income were experienced
before and after the change.[22] Because of this, the
compensation criterion could also sanction a movement
back from the resulting to the initial conditions.
Scitovsky proposed that this contradiction could be
eliminated if (a) the compensation criterion is satisfied and (b) those who are against the change are in-
capable of bribing those in favor to vote against it,
without losing much more than they would if the change
was carried.[23] If the compensation is actually paid,
this contradiction cannot arise. Scitovsky's criterion can be used to determine whether one situation
has greater economic welfare than another, but it is
not relevant to the question of which one has the
greater social welfare.

     P. A. Samuelson conceives of a social welfare
function which can assign a value to each and every
possible configuration of the social system.[24] This
implies that for each pair of social configurations,
we must be able to say either that one is better than
the other, or that they are the same. This implies
that if we made all pairwise comparisons, we should
obtain the best social system or a number of equally
good ones. The problem here is the determination of
who is to make the judgments between the selected
pairs of configurations.

     It is generally held that the compensation cri-
terion is not acceptable because it ignores income
distribution and that the Samuelson economic welfare
function is also unacceptable because it is impossible
to apply by virtue of its need for a "judge" to make
the choices.[25]

     Our discussion of social accounting and welfare
economics gives a fair idea of the difficulties en-
countered in trying to obtain a single measure of
societal performance. Many of the difficulties will
be overcome by the construction of two measures, one
for society and one for the individual, as will be
done in this book. Now that we have reviewed the
current state of affairs in the disciplines concerned

with general measures of societal performance, we
will turn our attention to social work, which is concerned with more specific programs and measures of
performance.

Social Work Research

The main thrust of social work research has been
in the development of methods of helping the individuals involved in various social programs and in the
administrative aspects of these programs. The review
which follows will consider only that literature which
deals with the measurement of the performance of social programs--a small but increasing part of social
work research.

The evaluation of social welfare programs is
usually treated as though the procedure can be divided into three parts: (a) identification of goals
and objectives (or selection of criterion variables),
(b) determination of the scope and extent of the effects of the program on the participants (or measurement of the changes in the criterion variables), (c)
evaluation of the value, importance, or utility of
(b), using (a) as a standard.

In reviewing current technology in social work
research, I will concentrate on the identification
of goals and objectives against which performance is
measured. I will not review the overall research
methodology currently available in which the measure
of performance or objective function is embedded,
since it is peripheral to the main thrust of this
book.

Goals of Welfare Programs As Measures of Success

When social scientists are asked to evaluate a
social welfare program, they usually depend upon the
explicitly stated goals of the organization that is
administering the program. Thus, they typically
treat the identification of goals and objectives as
outside the limits of scientific investigation. As
C. W. Churchman argues, "The notion of the limits of
science introduces a dualism which never seems to hold

up under the pressure of time. The dualism consists
of setting boundaries on the scope of human knowledge. It argues that this sort of question can be
studied scientifically, but that sort cannot. . . .
The dualism fails. . . . It claims to know enough
to know that a certain problem does not lie within
the scope of science. . . . Such a knowledge is
truly astounding."[26]

Continued abdication on the part of these social
scientists can do great harm to progress in this
area. As yet, to the best of my knowledge, no norm-
ative theory of goal formulation has been advanced,
although there have been worthwhile efforts made to
formulate objectives for welfare programs in specific
instances. F. S. Chapin has reviewed several such
studies.[27] Thus, most evaluation of welfare programs
has concentrated upon determining the effects of such
programs, using explicitly stated goals and objectives
to find the value of these effects. A notable excep-
tion is the work of J. Jahn, whose attempt to select
criterion variables statistically will be discussed
shortly.[28] I should now like to present a review of
the nature of currently used goals for welfare.

Implicit and Explicit Goals. While it may be
obvious that the specification of such evaluation
criteria should derive from the stated objectives of
the program concerned, in practice it usually does
not. One reason for this is that many programs have
implicit goals which differ (sometimes greatly) from
the explicitly stated goals attributed to the administrative organ. The explicitly stated goals are
usually quite vague--lacking any resemblance to the
operationally defined goals and objectives needed to
provide criteria for program evaluation. A few examples of explicit goals taken from various sources
are the following:

> "improve home conditions"[29]
> "control and prevent juvenile delinquency"[30]
> "improve human performance"[31]
> "improve community health and medical
>   services"[32]
> "encourage the care of dependent children"[33]

"strengthen family life"[34]
"promote the maintenance of a healthful
    environment"[35]
"foster self-reliance . . . enhance the
    dignity of the individual"[36]

The difficulty of selecting the criteria of
"success" for a welfare program depends upon the
vagueness of the explicit goals attributed to it,
while the difficulty involved in evaluating the results depends upon the amount of judgment used in
the criteria.

Objective and Subjective Criteria. As under-
standing about the nature of human poverty and despair has increased, individuals have tended to put
more emphasis upon subjective criteria commonly referred to as "tender-minded" in the evaluation of
welfare, as opposed to strictly objective or "tough-
minded" criteria.[37] In general, objective criteria
are more easily measured than subjective criteria.
For example, it is clear that a program aimed at reducing truancy can be more easily evaluated than a
program aimed at fostering self-reliance because
truancy can be defined as the number of days a stu-
dent was physically absent from classes without an
acceptable excuse, while self-reliance does not lend
itself so easily to a straightforward operational
definition. Tough-minded evaluators tend to attribute explicit goals (reduce truancy) to programs in
order to avoid measurement problems. Tender-minded
evaluators tend to attribute goals that are more general (reduce the desire for truancy) and more difficult to measure, or even to find measures for. Even
if the same goal is decided upon, the indicators
used as criteria will differ. Tough-minded researchers will tend toward no-nonsense, quantitative criteria, such as court appearances, arrest records, and
school grades, while tender-minded researchers will
tend toward "explanatory" criteria, such as hostility
levels, aspirations, and other intra-psychic factors.

Difficulties arise in each approach. In the
first, although the criteria selected usually have
the advantage of being easily measured, they may also

indicate symptoms or manifestations which can be altered without any effect on the causes of the problem.   (This is not to say that eliminating symptoms
is worthless; only that if the underlying causes are
left alone, recidivism becomes a problem.   Continual
suppression of symptoms may lead to new manifestations of an undesirable nature.) In the second, quantitative measures may be quite difficult to obtain,
but when found they possess the advantage of being
causal in the sense that if they are changed, a real
effect is observed.

Currently the tendency on the part of many researchers is to place increasing stress on the use of
simple, direct, and (hopefully) easily obtainable
criteria (tough-minded).   The main reason for this
trend is the seeming lack of measures for tender criteria.   I feel that this movement is counter to scientific advance as well as detrimental to welfare
evaluation.   S. S. Stevens' recent work indicates the
possibility of developing measures (interval- and
ratio-scaled) of such personal feelings as frustration
and aggression.[38]   Continued work in this area may
contribute to slowing and possibly reversing the trend
toward oversimplification.

In addition to subjective and objective criteria,
there are what I should like to call statistical criteria, that is, criteria selected in a statistical
manner.

Statistical Criteria. As previously mentioned,
Jahn has developed a method of evaluation based on
an application of statistical decision theory which
employs goals or "criterion variables," some of which
are selected a priori and some of which are selected
a posteriori.   Those selected a priori are called "Y
criterion" variables.   These are a result of a review of previous research and expert judgment.   The
second group, containing "X criterion" variables, is
selected from a list of potential variables based
upon the results of a statistical analysis of the
initial set of data collected.   Those potential variables which have significantly different values,
depending upon whether the individual is participating

in a welfare program or not, are selected. A number
of follow-up studies are then made and the resulting
data are analyzed, using the variables selected above.

This method has been applied in a study done
for the Community Service Society of New York on programs designed to serve the aged[39] and in a study of
alternative child welfare programs in Philadelphia.[40]

This concludes my review of the relevant state
of the art. The next two chapters will deal with the
development of a general statement of goals and objectives, from the point of view of the individual
and then from that of society.

NOTES

1. F. M. Cornford, trans., The Republic of
Plato (New York: Oxford University Press, 1958).
(First Edition, 15th Printing.)

2. F. J. E. Woodbridge, ed., Hobbes Selections
(New York: Charles Scribner's Sons, 1953), p. 134.

3. John Locke, "An Essay Concerning the True
Origin, Extent and End of Civil Government," E. A.
Burtt, ed., The English Philosophers from Bacon to
Mill (New York: Random House, 1939), p. 405.

4. R. L. Ackoff, Scientific Method (New York:
J. Wiley and Sons, 1962), p. 429.

5. E. A. Singer, On the Contented Life (New
York: H. Holt and Company, 1923), p. 109.

6. R. A. Bauer, Social Indicators (Cambridge,
Mass.: MIT Press, 1966), p. 1962.

7. O. Morgenstern, On the Accuracy of Economic
Observations (Princeton, N.J.: Princeton University
Press, 1950).

8. H. Schultz, The Theory and Measurement of
Demand (Chicago, University of Chicago Press, 1938);

J. W. Kendrick, <u>Productivity Trends in the United States</u> (Princeton, N.J.: Princeton University Press, 1961).

9.   A. D. Biderman, "Social Indicators and Goals," <u>Social Indicators</u> (Cambridge, Mass.: MIT Press, 1966).

10.   President's Research Committee on Social Trends, <u>Recent Social Trends in the United States</u> (New York: McGraw-Hill, 1933); President's Commission on National Goals, <u>Goals for Americans</u> (Englewood Cliffs, N.J.: Prentice-Hall, Inc., 1960).

11.   J. S. Mill, "Utilitarianism," E. A. Burtt, ed., <u>The English Philosophers from Bacon to Mill</u> (New York: Random House, 1939), p. 908.

12.   A. C. Pigou, <u>The Economics of Welfare</u> (London: Macmillan and Co., 1950).

13.   I. M. D. Little, <u>A Critique of Welfare Economics</u> (London: Oxford University Press, 1965), p. 9. (Second edition.)

14.   A. C. Pigou, <u>op. cit.</u>, p. 24.

15.   I. M. D. Little, <u>op. cit.</u>, p. 11.

16.   <u>Ibid.</u>, p. 84.

17.   <u>Ibid.</u>, p. 29.

18.   <u>Ibid.</u>, pp. 28-51.

19.   N. Kaldor, "Welfare Propositions of Economics and Interpersonal Comparisons of Utility," <u>The Economic Journal</u>, XLIX (September, 1939), p. 549.

20.   W. J. Baumol, "Community Indifference," <u>The Review of Economic Studies</u> (1946-47).

21.   J. R. Hicks, "The Rehabilitation of Consumer's Surplus," <u>The Review of Economic Studies</u>, VIII, 2 (1941), p. 108.

22. T. Scitovsky, "A Note on Welfare Propositions in Economics," The Review of Economic Studies,
IX, 2 (1941).

23. T. Scitovsky, "A Reconsideration of the
Theory of Tariffs," ibid.

24. P. A. Samuelson, Foundations of Economic
Analysis (Cambridge, Mass.: Harvard University
Press, 1947).

25. A detailed discussion of the applicability
of Samuelson's welfare function can be found in
I. M. D. Little, op. cit., Ch. 7.

26. C. W. Churchman, Prediction and Optimal
Decision (Englewood Cliffs, N.J.: Prentice-Hall,
Inc., 1961), p. 11.

27. F. S. Chapin, Experimental Design in Sociological Research (New York: Harper & Brothers,
1955).

28. J. Jahn, "The Statistical Definition of
Predicted Measures of Effectiveness of Alternative
Programs of Health, Education and Welfare" (Philadelphia: University of Pennsylvania, School of Social Work, 1965). (Mimeographed.)

29. Office of Economic Opportunity, Catalog
of Federal Programs for Individual and Community
Improvement (Washington, D.C.: Government Printing
Office, 1965), p. 139.

30. Ibid., p. 178.

31. Office of Economic Opportunity, Community
Action Program Guide, I (Washington, D.C.: Government
Printing Office, 1965), p. 21.

32. Department of Health, Education and Welfare,
Handbook on Programs (Washington, D.C.: Government
Printing Office, 1963), p. 54.

33.   Ibid., p. 194.

34.   Ibid., p. vii.

35.   Ibid., p. 23.

36.   Ibid., p. 230.

37.   See L. S. Kogan and A. W. Shyne, "Tender-Minded and Tough-Minded Approaches in Evaluative Research," Welfare in Review, IV, 2 (February, 1966), p. 12.

38.   S. S. Stevens, "A Metric for the Social Consensus," Science, CLI (1966).

39.   J. Jahn and M. Blenkner, Serving the Aging, Methodological Supplement--Part I--Experimental Design and Statistical Tests of Hypotheses   (New York: Community Service Society of New York, 1964).

40.   J. Jahn and B. A. Gelin, Philadelphia Child Welfare Project: Research Design for Phase I, 1965-66 (Philadelphia: Research Center, School of Social Work, University of Pennsylvania, 1966).

CHAPTER **3** FORMULATION OF
SOCIAL GOALS FROM
AN INDIVIDUALISTIC
VIEWPOINT

INTRODUCTION

In this chapter, as well as in the following
one, philosophical ideas will be developed into operational measures of the performance of social programs.
In Chapter 4, the measure will be based directly upon
societal goals, while here it will be based upon individual goals.

The philosophical ideas central to this chapter
were held by such philosophers as Kant and Bentham.
Kant's basic position was that man is an end unto himself,[1] while Bentham's works centered on his belief
in the principle of the greatest good for the greatest number.[2] Actually, this notion of Bentham's is
a way to approximate the state that would arise under
a Kantian system. Many other philosophers have held
that the interests of the individual are supreme; I
take this position as a starting point.

In this chapter a measure of the "good" society
does for an individual by means of a specific welfare
program will be formulated. Actually, the analysis
which will be presented could apply to any societal
action, which may or may not be in the form of an organized effort or program. Let the jth program be
denoted as Pj. A program may affect an individual
in two different ways—it may change either the environment in which he lives or his responses to that
environment.

THE ENVIRONMENT OR STATE DEFINED

The individual lives in an environment which consists of other individuals, objects--tangible or intangible--and relationships among the individuals and objects. I will be concerned with a certain subset of these objects, individuals, and relationships. Each individual has both real and perceived needs for some subset of the objects contained in the environment. (The term "need" should be read in its usual sense. It describes the relationship that exists between the individual and his operating environment.) Let this subset of objects for which the individual has a need comprise the individual's operating environment. Let O_{ik}: $i = 1, 2, \ldots, m$ be the objects comprising the kth individual's operating environment. Let $n_{ik}(t)$ be a measure of the degree to which the kth individual's need for the ith object is satisfied at time t. The state the kth individual is in at time t, $S_k(t)$, may then be described by the column vector

$$S_k(t) = [n_{ik}(t)]; \ i = 1, 2, \ldots, m.$$

The objects in an individual's operating environment can be taken either as externally identified or as perceived by the individual himself.

The first way that a program can affect an individual is by changing his environment, i.e., changing the state he is in. This would necessarily change the levels of satisfaction the individual experiences with respect to at least one of the objects he needs.

The other way a program can affect an individual is by changing his responses to his environment when the relative values or utilities of the $[n_{ik}(t)]$ change. Denote the utility of a set of $n_{ik}(t)$ by $U[S_k(t)]$. A change in $U[S_k(t)]$ can be readily understood and needs no explanation. A useful definition of the $n_{ik}(t)$'s will now be presented, followed by presentation of a model of an individual's evaluation procedure, which will have a central role in the development of a measure of the performance of a welfare program.

AN OPERATIONAL DEFINITION OF
LEVEL OF SATISFACTION

An operational definition is one which should
"be directive . . . should tell the researcher how
to investigate that which is conceptualized."[3] Included in the act of operationally defining a concept
is the complete specification of the procedures necessary for its realization. An objective operational
measure of the level of satisfaction an individual
experiences with respect to a need for a given object
will slowly unfold, as will other necessary definitions. The measure will be objective in the usual
sense, i.e., two researchers, if they are following
the outlined procedures, should observe the same level
of satisfaction.

It should be remembered in the following discussion that when one thinks of a level of satisfaction,
a specific object is implied. Although it is quite
simple to extend this concept to many objects, it is
not necessary to do so because a procedure for combining them will also be presented. Objects should
be considered as broadly as possible. They include
physical objects, actions, and feelings or emotions.
Objects can be possessed in varying degrees: some
are indivisible, some come in discrete amounts, and
some are available in continuous quantities. For example, an individual either has or does not have a
job, has an integer number of rooms in his home, and
has a certain measurable caloric intake. For simplicity I will consider all objects as capable of being
quantified in discrete amounts called units, which
naturally are different for each object.

It is recognized that the value a given individual places upon an amount (or number of units) of a
given object depends upon the amounts already po-
sessed, not only of the given object but also of other
objects. While these interrelationships are quite
easy to express symbolically, they would render any
application of this model next to impossible. It is
for this reason that the objects are considered as
independent. (Objects are considered as independent
when the marginal utility of an additional unit is
unaffected by the amounts possessed of other objects.)

A good approximation of independence can be achieved
if one combines objects which are substitutable or
complementary into one object. For example, butter
and margarine are substitutable; coffee and sugar are
complementary.

In order to obtain an operational definition of
the term "level of satisfaction," a preliminary definition, that of the term "saturated," is necessary.
Let "saturated" be defined as follows:

> Place an individual in a situation in which
> he has a choice between two courses of ac-
> tion, neither of which is preferred per se.
> The first course of action leads with cer-
> tainty to an outcome containing a number of
> units of an object. The second course of
> action also leads with certainty to an out-
> come identical to the above, except that it
> contains an additional unit of the object.
> Repeat, each time adding a unit to the lat-
> ter environment until the individual does
> not consistently select either course of
> action (i.e., is indifferent). (By "con-
> sistently," it is meant that the probabil-
> ity of selection of a course of action is
> significantly different from 0.5.) Then,
> the individual is said to be saturated with
> respect to the object.

Denote the number of units in the former environment when the kth individual is saturated with
the ith object at time t as $N_{ik}(t)$, and the number
of units the kth individual actually possesses at
time t as $N'_{ik}(t)$. Now the level of satisfaction can
be defined as follows:

The level of satisfaction, $n_{ik}(t)$, or the degree
to which the kth individual is satisfied with respect
to the ith object, is equal to the ratio $N'_{ik}(t)/N_{ik}(t)$.

An object and its level of satisfaction have
been defined in such a way that the latter can be
measured objectively. In a real situation an individual's perception of his level of satisfaction may
differ considerably from an objective measure of his

level of satisfaction either because of his lack of
knowledge of the existence of certain objects or be-
because of his lack of knowledge of his possession
of certain objects.

At this point in our discussion we have operationally defined the level of satisfaction, $n_{ik}(t)$,
and the state the individual is in at time t, $S_k(t)$.
It remains to define the relative importance, $\Psi_k(t)$,
of the objects to the individual. This concept is
used in determining the utility of a given state,
$U[S_k(t)]$, to the individual.

THE UTILITY OR VALUE OF A STATE

The utility of a state to the kth individual,
denoted by $U[S_k(t)]$, is equal to a function of the
levels of satisfaction the individual experiences
with respect to his needs for various objects. This
function employs $\Psi_k(t)$, the relative importance of
each of these various objects, which is a column
vector with m components, $\Psi_k(t) = [\psi_{ik}(t)]$. Thus,
the levels of satisfaction the individual experiences,
when weighted by the relative importance of the various objects to which they apply and then added, yield
the utility of the state that is described by these
levels of satisfaction. Thus, a prerequisite for a
knowledge of the utility of the state is knowledge
of the relative importance of the various objects in
the individual's operating environment.

The relative importance of the various objects
at a given time t, $\Psi(t)$, is conditional upon the
state the individual is in at time t, $S_k(t)$. That
is, it depends upon what he currently possesses.
This conditional evaluation should be recognized as
implicitly including both the utility of the various
current levels of satisfaction and the importance of
the objects themselves.

Definition of the Relative Importance
of an Object

Let the m objects be $O_1, \ldots, O_m$, each of which is
possessed in amount $N'_i(t)$ at time t by an individual.

Denote an additional unit of each object as $\Delta O_1, \ldots, \Delta O_m$. Next, using a method of measuring approximate value developed by Churchman and Ackoff and presented in Appendix A, assign a value to each ΔO_1. Normalize these values by expressing them as a percentage of their total and denote these normalized values as $\psi_{ik}(t)$ for the ith ΔO and the kth individual at time t.

Definition of the Utility of a State

The levels of satisfaction which describe a state should be multiplied by the vector $\Psi_k(t)$ and summed over objects to yield the utility of the state described by the levels of satisfaction. Thus, the utility of a state, $U[S_k(t)]$, to the kth individual is

$$U[S_k(t)] = \Psi_k^T(t)S_k(t) = \sum_{i=1}^{m} \psi_{ik}(t)n_{ik}(t).$$

At this point, the components of the model are completely specified. It should be noted that the amount of each object possessed may affect the $\psi_{ik}(t)$ and that one might say that the values of $\Psi_k(t)$ are dependent upon the possessions of the individual. This is to say that the relative importance of the objects may be affected by the levels of satisfaction. (The reason for this is that objects which are possessed may be less important than those not possessed or, due to the necessity of reducing cognitive dissonance, more important.) This is reasonable, since by "relative importance" I mean the relative importance of the objects to the individual.

Using this method, one can determine the utility of a program or societal action, $U_k(P_j)$, to the kth individual. One difficulty which will arise is that the individual's feelings for future states beyond t*, the time when the evaluation occurs, are not taken into consideration. Unfortunately, I know of no reasonable way to correct this situation except, perhaps, to evaluate a program with a sample of individuals and monitor the effects over a long period of time. Using this sample, generalize the results to make estimates of the value of states occurring after

t* by using the value of $S_k(t)$ as the independent
variable in a regression equation.

MODEL OF AN INDIVIDUAL'S EVALUATION PROCEDURE

The following is a brief description of the
model depicted in Figure 1.   This model states that
an individual, I_k, is in a given state, $S_k(t)$, at
time t.   Further, a program, P_j, affects an individual by changing either this state or the utility of
this state to the individual. $U_k[P_j]$, the utility
to the kth individual of the jth program, is the
difference between the utility of the state the individual was in before the program began, $U[S_k(t)]$,
and the utility of the state the individual is in
after the program ends, $U[S_k(t^*)]$.   Naturally, the
utility of the states depends upon changes in the
actual or perceived levels of $n_{ik}(t)$ and the relative
value of the objects involved.   ($\Psi_k(t^*)$ refers to a
vector of $\Psi_{ik}(t^*)$ determined at the time of the evaluation in the same way as $\Psi_k(t)$ is determined before
the program begins.)   The following relationships
hold:

$$S_k(t) \qquad = [n_{ik}(t)]; \; i=1,2\ldots$$

$$S_k(t^*) \qquad = [n_{ik}(t^*)]$$

$$U[S_k(t)] \qquad = \Psi_k^T(t) \cdot S_k(t)$$

$$U[S_k(t^*)] \quad = \Psi_k^T(t^*) \cdot S_k(t^*)$$

$$U_k[P_j] \qquad = U[S_k(t^*)] - U[S_k(t)].$$

In more detail, then, a program affects an individual by changing the levels of satisfaction he
experiences and by changing the relative importance
of the objects in his operating environment.   The
altered levels of satisfaction define the state,
$S_k(t^*)$.   When the relative importance of the various
objects, $\Psi_k(t^*)$, is taken into consideration, the
utility of the state the individual is in at the time
of evaluation, $U[S_k(t^*)]$, can be determined.   When
$U[S_k(t)]$ is subtracted from this, the measure of the

FIGURE I

Model of the Individual's Evaluation Procedure

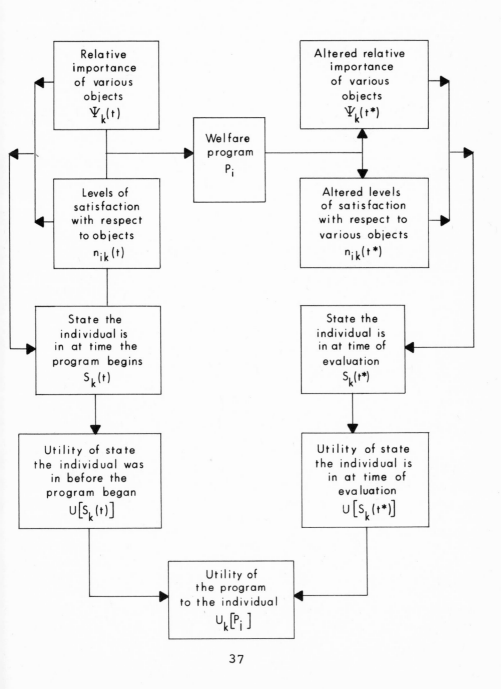

utility of the jth program's contribution to each of
the participating individuals, $U_k[P_j]$, is obtained.

USE OF THE MODEL TO EVALUATE PROGRAMS

Once the gain in utility of a particular program
to an individual is found for each of the individuals
participating in that program, a frequency distribution of these gains can be constructed. This distribution can be used to give an objective measure of
the program's contribution to the set of individuals
involved. Implicit in forming a distribution of individual utilities is the assumption of equality of
individuals, that one person is exactly as important
as another.

Once a distribution of individuals' utilities
for a given program is obtained, some measure of central tendency can be employed to measure the utility
of the program. I shall use the mean. (Another
measure of central tendency which has desirable properties is the median, since at least 50 percent of
the participating individuals have experienced a value
at least this high.) Thus,

$$U(P_j) = \int_{-\infty}^{\infty} U\, f_j(U)\, dU,$$

where $f_j(U)$ is the distribution of individuals' utilities for those persons participating in the jth program. (Individuals not actually participating in the
program may be affected by it. This would be the
case if certain individuals in a neighborhood were
assisted and others were not. Some individuals might
benefit through information transmitted by friends
in the program. In other cases, jealousy could result. All individuals who are affected by a program
should be considered as participants; however, so
inclusive a definition will not be used in most practical situations.) Use of this measure assumes that
the variance of individual utilities is not large or
that distributional efforts are not important.

In this chapter I have developed an operational
procedure which will result in a measure of a program's

utility for individuals. This measure is based upon
the degree to which the individual's needs for objects are satisfied. A distribution of these utilities is formed on the basis of the assumption of
equality of individuals, and the mean of this distribution is used as a measure of the utility of the
program.

In the next chapter a discussion leading to a
formulation of the goals of a democratic society will
be presented, along with measures of the degree to
which these goals are currently being attained. These
concepts will be used to measure the contribution of
welfare programs from the point of view of society.

NOTES

1. I. Kant, "Foundations of the Metaphysics
of Morals," Critique of Practical Reason and Other
Writings (Chicago: University of Chicago Press,
1949), p. 86.

2. J. Bentham, "An Introduction to the Princi-
ples of Morals and Legislation," E. A. Burtt, ed.,
The English Philosophers from Bacon to Mill (New
York: Random House, 1939), p. 791.

3. R. L. Ackoff, Scientific Method (New York:
J. Wiley and Sons, 1962), p. 15.

4

FORMULATION OF
SOCIAL GOALS FROM
A SOCIETAL VIEWPOINT

INTRODUCTION

In Chapter 2 the desirability of the formulation of both an individualistic and a societal welfare function was established. An ideal individualistic function was set up in Chapter 3, and now an ideal societal function will be discussed. A succeeding chapter will be concerned with making these functions operational, in particular with the approximation methods needed for their actual application.

I shall presently define a "state of society." A societal welfare function is a mapping of the possible states of society into the real line. It can be symbolically expressed as

$$\Lambda(w): w \epsilon \, \Omega \rightarrow r \epsilon \, R,$$

which reads $\Lambda(w)$, the societal welfare function, is a mapping from the set of all states of society, Ω, to the real numbers R. Thus, to each state of society there corresponds a unique real number. It is possible, however, for two w's to correspond to the same r. We can represent this function graphically, as in Figure 2.

In this chapter I shall first describe the various states of society and then develop a societal welfare function, $\Lambda(w)$, using these descriptions. Later I shall use this function as a basis for the evaluation of particular programs from the point of view of society.

FIGURE 2

Graphic Representation of Societal Welfare Function

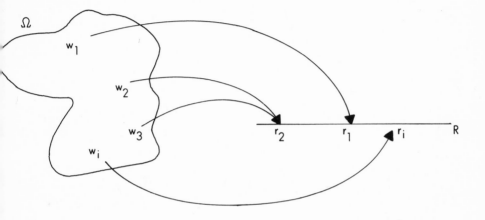

THE NATURE AND ORIGIN OF SOCIETAL GOALS

A description of a state of society may be based upon many different variables, depending upon what factors the describer deems important. In Chapter 2 a very brief review of social accounting was presented. It should be obvious from that discussion that any useful method of social accounting must be founded upon a set of assumptions about the goals and objectives of society.

As stated in Chapter 2, there are several views on the nature of societal goals. One view formulates them in terms of an aggregate of individual goals, subject to some reasonable constraints. I believe, however, that this is not a promising approach, because societal goals cannot really be expressed as an aggregate of individual goals, nor are they even of a similar nature. Individual goals pertain to

the attainment of specific objects, while societal
goals may be thought of as pertaining to the attainment of the means of obtaining. I have arrived at
this conclusion via the following route.

Suppose, as initially seems reasonable, that we
argue that only from individuals' goals we can obtain
societal goals. One could distinguish between goals
belonging to society and those not belonging to society by considering those individual goals which
are in the "public interest" as societal goals. In
a democratic society, public interest refers to the
goals of all persons in the society. In more authoritarian forms of government, public interest refers
only to a subset of such persons. In either case,
we quickly come to an impasse because the goals in
question ought to refer not only to present members
of society but also to future members. A society is
a dynamic entity and should not be defined in terms
of a single cross section in time. While it might
be possible to try to guess the goals of future members of society, such attempts would suffer from
their very nature. They would be based upon established patterns and would, therefore, contain all the
limitations of our present point of view.

There is, however, a way out of this predica-
ment. This is to abandon individual goals and to
state societal goals in a general form, so that they
will be sufficiently adaptable to be in the public
interest under any conditions.

Remembering that public interest refers to all
persons in a democratic society but to only a subset
in an authoritarian society, I shall next consider
the democratic society only. I shall first formulate
a set of meta-goals for a democratic society, a set
of broad philosophical principles. Then I will de-
vise the operating goals of a democratic society from
the statement of these meta-goals. If one were to
carry through the same process for various undemo-
cratic societies, the goals and meta-goals would be
similar in form but would be qualified everywhere
with statements restricting the set of persons to
whom the goals were to be applied and the degree to
which they were intended to be realized.

A STATEMENT OF META-GOALS

The terms "end" and "non-destructive end" are used in the statement of meta-goals. I should like to define them at this point.

And end is a future state ($S_k(t)$, as defined in Chapter 3, "Introduction") in which an individual desires to be, while a non-destructive end is one which, if realized, will result in a state of society in which $U[S_k(t')] - U[S_k(t)] \geq 0$; $\forall_k$, where $S_k(t')$ is a state in which the end is realized, and $S_k(t)$ is a state in which the end is not realized. An alternative definition of a non-destructive end would involve a summation of individual utilities. If $\sum [U(S_k(t')) - U(S_k(t))]$ is positive, then the end would be considered non-destructive. This way of defining a non-destructive end may seem more practical, but it does not put one on a Pareto frontier, as is desirable in an ideal situation.

My concept of the meta-goals appropriate for a democratic society is based on an idea which was clearly stated by Singer. He felt that there was one desire fundamental to all desires, the desire for the ability to attain any end which one might want: "The condition of attaining any end which one might want is such control of the world's machinery as shall give you power to get what you want."[1] I shall proceed along these lines, defining meta-goals for a democratic society which assume that society's role is to help individuals toward their particular goals and to resolve by compromise any conflicts that arise in the process.

I shall adopt the following three meta-goals for a democratic society.

1. To provide the necessary machinery such that for each non-destructive end there exists a course of action which leads to the attainment of that end.

2. To provide every member of society with the knowledge, equal opportunity, and

resources needed to enable him to make
use of the existing machinery.

3. To provide stimuli to help each indi-
    vidual perceive new non-destructive ends.

These are meta-goals in the sense that they provide
a rational framework within which the set of societal
goals becomes meaningful. Before presenting a statement of the operating goals of society, which I will
obtain from these meta-goals, I will discuss the
ways in which a democratic society attempts to attain
these meta-goals.

THE ROLE AND GOALS OF A DEMOCRATIC SOCIETY

Just exactly what role society should have in
relation to the individual has been much debated. I
intend to avoid this issue here (my feelings are ap-
parent from Chapter 3), and will merely make some
observations on the role society does play in its
interactions with individuals. The following discussion is written as if society possessed a rational
mind and actively made and implemented decisions.
This is probably a good approximation of the situation when the time span considered is sufficiently
long. In the same sense that the human mind is made
up of millions of individual cells, each capable of
making certain decisions and of working in consort,
in some unknown way, to produce what we call thought,
so society is comprised of millions of individuals
working together in some way to make decisions. To
the individual cells an actual thought may span a
lifetime, and so may it be with a social thought and
an individual.

All societies attempt to provide some of their
members with services designed to facilitate the attainment of their respective ends. Most of the services society currently performs are aimed at accom-
plishing one or more of the following:[2]

1. inspiring
2. manufacturing

3. distributing
4. providing
5. protecting.

Modern society tends to operate mainly through cen-
tralized governmental bodies, although it also exerts
its influence through quasi-establishment organs
(formal or informal groups of individuals), such as
organized religions, the private enterprise system,
communications media, and educational institutions.

The operating goals of society can be expressed
in terms of the successful performance of its functions, specifically the five mentioned above.

A Set of Operating Goals

After clarifying the meaning of some of the included terms, I will present a set of five operating
goals for a democratic society which correspond to
the functions listed above.

It should be remembered from Chapter 3 that
"objects" may be either tangible or intangible enti-
ties. An object may be a household article, a personal relationship, or even a mood or feeling.
"Inspiring" is the undertaking by society of any action which attempts to change the utility an individual has for a given state. The words "manufacturing"
and "distributing" are used in a similar vein. Thus,
one could speak of manufacturing and distributing
relationships and moods, as well as of manufacturing
and distributing goods and services. "Resources"
(as employed below in the statement of the operating
goals of society) should also be broadly defined, to
include such intangibles as points of view, mental
blocks, and initiative. An object is considered to
be accessible to an individual if, given adequate
resources to possess it, he can possess it.

The five operating goals based on the meta-goals
previously listed of a democratic society are

1. To inspire each member of society to
    seek only non-destructive ends.

2. To manufacture an adequate amount of
    each object so that it is possible for
    each individual to possess the objects
    constituting his operating environment.

3. To distribute objects and information
    so that the existing objects are acces-
    sible to all.

4. To provide each member of society with
    sufficient resources to be able to pos-
    sess the accessible objects which are
    contained in his need sets.

5. To protect each member of society from
    the denial of objects, and to protect
    his access to objects and resources
    for possessing them as long as they con-
    stitute elements of his set of non-
    destructive ends.

The state which society is in at a given time t,
w(t), should be expressed in terms of the degree to
which each of the above goals has been realized. But
before this can be done, measures of the degree to
which each of these goals is being realized must be
formulated. It should be noted again that the equality of individuals is implicit in the above discussion. The term "each member" embodies within it the
concept of equal opportunity. Thus the measures that
are presented below are invariant under changes in
the labeling of individuals.

IDEAL MEASURES OF THE DEGREE TO WHICH EACH
OPERATING GOAL OF SOCIETY IS REALIZED

The degree to which the first goal of society is
realized is a function both of the number of destructive ends each individual maintains and their relative
destructiveness. Put another way, the degree to which
the first goal of society is realized is inversely
proportional to the total relative disutility of the
destructive ends which have been realized by individuals. Let $I(t)$ be the degree to which the first goal

of society is being realized at time t, then, more directly,

$$I(t) = \frac{\sum\limits_{k=1}^{n(t)} U[S_k(t)]}{\sum\limits_{k=1}^{n(t)} U[S_k(t'')]},$$

where $S_k(t)$ is the state in which the kth individual actually is, and $S_k(t'')$ is that state in which only non-destructive ends are realized for the kth individual and for which $U[S_k(t'')]$ is as small as possible. To show that $I(t) \leq 1$ we note that since $S_k(t'')$ is a non-destrictive end,

$$U[S_k(t)] \leq U[S_k(t'')], \quad \forall_k .$$

Thus,

$$\sum\limits_{k=1}^{n(t)} U[S_k(t)] \leq \sum\limits_{k=1}^{n(t)} U[S_k(t'')],$$

from which $I(t) \leq 1$ immediately follows.

The degree to which the second goal of society is realized is a function of the ratio of the number of goods which are manufactured to those which are desired. Let $M(t)$ be the degree to which the second goal of society is realized at time t, where

$$M(t) = \frac{\sum\limits_{i=1}^{m(t)} \Pi_i(t)}{\sum\limits_{i=1}^{m(t)} \sum\limits_{k=1}^{n(t)} N_{ik}(t)} .$$

$N_{ik}(t)$ is the number of units of the ith object needed to saturate the kth individual at time t, $\Pi_i(t)$ is the total number of units of the ith object produced at time t, and $m(t)$ is the number of different objects at time t. (When $M(t) > 1$, we have a

condition of overproduction, which can be expected to
have harmful results. These will show up later in
Λ (t) because of the wasted resources, which could
have been used to increase the other measures.

The degree to which the third goal of society
is realized is a function of the proportion of times
that goods are accessible. Let D(t) be the degree
to which the third goal of society is realized at
time t, where

$$D(t) = \sum_{i=1}^{m(t)} \sum_{k=1}^{n(t)} P_{ik}(t).$$

$P_{ik}(t)$ is the probability that the ith object will
be available to the kth individual at time t if the
individual has a need for it.

The degree to which the fourth goal of society
is realized is a function of the number of objects
that cannot be possessed because of the lack of resources held by the individual. Let R(t) be the degree to which the fourth goal of society is being
realized at time t, where

$$R(t) = \frac{\sum_{i=1}^{m(t)} \sum_{i=1}^{n(t)} N'_{ik}(t)}{\sum_{i=1}^{m(t)} \sum_{k=1}^{n(t)} N''_{ik}(t)}.$$

$N''_{ik}(t)$ is the needed amount of the ith object which
could be possessed by the kth individual if he had
adequate resources, and $N'_{ik}(t)$ is the amount actually possessed.

The degree to which the fifth goal of society
is realized is a function of the disutility caused by
the denial of the existing courses of action. Let
$S_k^*(t)$ be a non-destructive end denied to the kth
individual, and let $S_k(t)$ be his current state. We
can express the degree to which the fifth goal of
society is reached by P(t), where:

$$P(t) = \frac{\sum\limits_{k=1}^{n(t)} U[S_k(t)]}{\sum\limits_{k=1}^{n(t)} U[S^*_k(t)]}$$

A measure of the degree to which each of the five goals of society has been realizes has now been presented.

COMBINING THE MEASURES TO ACHIEVE A SOCIETAL WELFARE FUNCTION

In Chapter 3 we saw that the state that society is in can be expressed in terms of the number of individual members of society, the number of objects available, and the levels of satisfaction and utilities of the levels of satisfaction that the individuals experience. Thus, $w(t)$ can be expressed as a vector with the following four components:

$$w(t) = \left[n(t), \ \sum_i N_i(t), \ \sum_k S_k(t), \ \sum_k U[S_k(t)] \right] .$$

In this chapter I have developed another way of expressing the state of society in vector form, although here I have adopted a much different point of view. I might have explicitly included $n(t)$ in this formulation, but I chose not to do so because it is implicitly expressed in the other components of the vector,

$$w(t) = \left[I(t), \ M(t), \ D(t), \ R(t), \ P(t) \right] .$$

Earlier in this chapter I spoke of a societal welfare function as a mapping of Ω, the set of all states of society, into the real line. We must now face the question of how this mapping is to be constructed. This is an important question because when we wish to compare the results of several alternative welfare programs, which is the ultimate aim of this book, it will be very convenient to have the values of these programs represented on a unidimensional scale.

There are various methods which can be employed
to express a multidimensional value in a single dimension or to reduce the dimensionality of a value
while retaining certain properties of the relationships among the vector components in the original
number of dimensions. It is not within the scope of
this study to review all of these methods, but some
comment on the types of methods is in order.

A Basis for Combining the Measures

Without intending to demean the labors of many
researchers, particularly those involved in market
research, no method of reducing dimensionality can
claim to be a valid one unless such a method is
based upon the discovery of the underlying relationships which exist among the vector components. Therefore, it would be natural to turn our attention to
the problem of investigating the underlying relationships among the five components, $I(t)$, $M(t)$, $D(t)$,
$R(t)$, and $P(t)$. Actually, we are searching for a framework in which the relationships can be fruitfully expressed. Such a framework does exist, and a param-
eter of this framework provides us with the link con-
necting the components of $w(t)$. This framework,
familiar to operations researchers, is the process
of rational decision making. The components of this
process are courses of action, outcomes, and utilities of outcomes, as well as the probabilities of
selecting various courses of action and the conditional probabilities, given each course of action,
that an outcome will in fact occur.

Consider the specific situation in which the
outcomes are an individual's non-destructive ends.
In the decision-making process presented above, the
conditional probabilities of obtaining ends (outcomes) through given actions are usually referred to
as efficiencies. I feel that each of the components
of $w(t)$ is directly related both to efficiencies and
to the probabilities that courses of action are selected. Thus, a valid method of reducing the dimensionality of $w(t)$ would be to transform the components
of $w(t)$ into its contributions to these probabilities
and efficiencies. That these relationships do exist

can be demonstrated by reviewing each of the five
components and its possible effect upon the efficiencies of alternative courses of action. We shall
next show how this framework can be used to obtain
a unidimensional measure for w(t) in this situation.

Use of the Decision-Making Model in Obtaining a Unidimensional Measure

The value of a given situation to an individual
can be determined if the following parameters are
known or can be estimated:

     a.   available courses of action
     b.   the probability that an individual
          will select each of the courses of
          action
     c.   the possible outcomes
     d.   the utility of the outcome to the
          individual
     e.   the efficiency of a course of action
          in resulting in an outcome.

The value of the situation for an individual is, of
course, the following expectation:

$$V_k = \sum_i \sum_j p_i E_{ij} U(o_j),$$

where

p_i = probability of the ith course of
        action being selected

E_{ij} = efficiency of the ith course of action
        in resulting in the jth outcome

$U(o_j)$ = utility of jth outcome.

In the above situation it would be difficult to
separate the effects of various components of the
vector w(t) upon p_i and E_{ij}. In an effort to sim-
plify matters, I will combine these two into one.
Let the effectiveness of a course of action in obtaining an outcome be defined as $\mathscr{E}_{ij}$, where
$$\mathscr{E}_{ij} = p_i E_{ij}.$$

The value of the situation to an individual can now
be expressed as

$$V_k = \sum_i \sum_j \mathcal{E}_{ij} \; U(o_j).$$

The utility of a non-destructive end can, of course,
be expressed as the utility of a state in which it
is achieved. Thus, we will wish to replace $U(o_j)$
with $U[S_k^*(t)]$, which is the utility of the state in
which all the individual's needs are saturated. Now
V_k can be replaced with the value of the state the
individual is currently in. Thus, the state of society and the state of the individual may be related
through $\mathcal{E}_{ij}$. A transformation of the vector $w(t)$
may be accomplished directly by finding a function
of $w(t)$, η_k, such that

$$U[S_k(t)] = \eta_k \; (w(t)) \; . \; U[S_k^*(t)].$$

Ordinarily regression analysis would be used to find
a suitable η_k. The value of the societal welfare
function for a given individual would then be

$$\Lambda_k \; (w) = \eta_k.$$

If η_k is to take the form of a sum of weights, each
of which is proportional to the effect which each of
the five components has upon $\mathcal{E}_{ij}$, then we can express
η_k as follows. (The η_k could be explicitly time-
subscribed if desired; as is, they are implicitly so.)

$$\eta_k = \eta_k \; (I) + \eta_k \; (M) + \eta_k \; (D) + \eta_k \; (R) + \eta_k \; (P),$$

where

$\quad\quad \eta_k(I) \quad$ is proportional to the effect of $I(t)$
$\quad\quad\quad\quad\quad$ upon V_k

$\quad\quad \eta_k(M) \quad$ is proportional to the effect of $M(t)$
$\quad\quad\quad\quad\quad$ upon V_k

$\quad\quad \eta_k(D) \quad$ is proportional to the effect of $D(t)$
$\quad\quad\quad\quad\quad$ upon V_k

$\eta_k(R)$ is proportional to the effect of R(t) upon V_k

$\eta_k(P)$ is proportional to the effect of P(t) upon V_k.

Thus, we can express $\Lambda_k(w)$, the value of the societal welfare function for the kth individual, as

$$\Lambda_k(w) = \eta_k (I) + \eta_k (M) + \eta_k (D) + \eta_k (R) + \eta_k (P).$$

Distributional Considerations

This procedure has transformed $\Lambda_k(w)$ into a unidimensional value. At this point one could still object by pointing out that we have a distribution of values over individuals. However, many alternative statistics have been developed for use as measures of central tendency (mean, median, mode, interquartile average) for the purposes of comparison. The choice of such a measure of central tendency now becomes important. Naturally there are arguments for and against each of the measures of central tendency.

What I propose is a weighted mean using a special form of weighting function, call it g ($\Lambda_k(w)$), yielding a mean, Λ, for a program where

$$\Lambda = \int_{-\infty}^{\infty} g (\Lambda_k(w)) \Lambda_k(w) \, dw .$$

This weighting function has been dubbed a "fairness function." Different forms of this function can be constructed to correspond to various points of view. The philosophy behind the development of this weighting function is as follows.

Programs can have large variations in effect. Sometimes certain persons will be helped greatly, while others may even be harmed. I feel that, by and large, a program with a great deal of variation in effect is less desirable than a program having the same mean effect and less variation. Consequently,

the fairness function should penalize programs which
have large dispersions in their contributions to individuals.   The fairness function can assume various
shapes, some of which are presented in Figure 3.
Function (a) is a limiting case; it is equivalent to
using only the mean value of the distribution for the
purposes of comparing program effects.   Function (b)
penalizes for extremes in either direction.   In other
words, a program which helps a small number of people
is, in this case, considered as desirable as a program which harms a small number of people, provided
the two have the same mean effect.   Function (c)
penalizes only for those extreme values below the
mean; hence, programs which are extremely good for
a few people are preferred to those which are extremely bad for a few people, given the same mean effect.

A fairness function of form (c) should be used
for the following reasons.   A function of form (a)
can be a limiting case of (b) or (c), and thus can
be removed from consideration on the grounds that it
is redundant.   Consider two alternative programs
which result in two distributions which are identical
save for one value.   Further, let this value be equal
to the mean or above for one program and higher for
the other program.   Function (b) may result in a
value of $\Lambda(w)$ which is higher for the first program.
Clearly, this is not a desirable property for such
a function to have.   This leaves us with a function
of type (c).   One does not, however, need to select
a particular fairness function.   A discussion of this
point will be found in Chapter 6, which deals with
the application of the societal welfare function to
the evaluation of alternative programs.

SUMMARY

In this chapter the meta-goals of a democratic
society were presented.   From this statement five
goals of such a society were developed.   Each of the
five was operationally defined and accompanied by a
measure of the degree to which it was realized. These
efforts resulted in the vector $w(t) = [I(t), M(t),$
$D(t), R(t), P(t)]$.   Next, a consideration of efforts

FIGURE 3

Alternative Fairness Functions

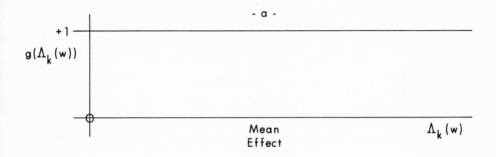

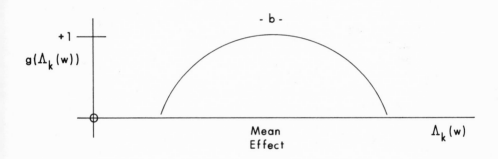

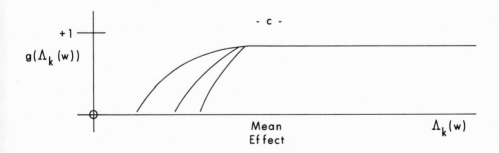

to reduce w(t) to one dimension was undertaken. It
was reduced by means of a transformation based upon
what was believed to be causal relationships among
the five components of w(t). The validity of such
a transformation is inherent in its formulation.

The unidimensional measure $\Lambda_k(w)$ can be used
to evaluate the effectiveness of a given welfare program from the societal point of view. A measure of
the participants' contribution to $\Lambda_k(w)$ can be obtained both before and after the program while the
same measures are obtained for a control group. The
differences between the measures taken at two points
in time, say $\Delta\Lambda_k(1)$ for the program participants and
$\Delta\Lambda_k(2)$ for the control group, can then be compared
and tested.

Before moving on to the development of approximations to both the individualistic and societal
functions, it should be mentioned that societies
which have different sets of meta-goals would probably, although not necessarily, show different sets
of goals. Thus, the vector components of w(t) which
lead to a single measure of societal achievement
would differ. It is my opinion that the fairness
function is a robust concept which would apply in
all cases, although not necessarily in form (c).
Thus, the development of w(t) and $\Lambda_k(w)$ in this
chapter is merely one example of a general process.
I feel that the example chosen, a democratic society,
is a particularly important one.

Chapter 5 will discuss approximations that will
be desirable, indeed necessary, in employing the
measures developed in this chapter and the preceding
one in the evaluation of the effectiveness of a welfare program.

NOTES

1. E. A. Singer, On the Contented Life (New
York: H. Holt and Company, 1936), p. 109.

2. R. L. Ackoff, Scientific Method (New York:
J. Wiley and Sons, 1962), p. 431.

5 DEVELOPING APPROXIMATE
MEASURES OF SOCIETAL
PERFORMANCE--FROM
INDIVIDUAL AND COLLECTIVE
VIEWPOINTS

THE NEED FOR AND USE OF APPROXIMATIONS

In Chapter 3 we saw that the value or utility of
a program, $U(P_j)$, can be expressed as the mean, or
other measure of central tendency, of a distribution
of individual utilities, $U_k(P_j)$, for the program,
providing that the variance of this distribution is
small. In Chapter 4 we saw that from a particular
statement of meta-goals, those of a democratic society, we could develop five societal goals accompanied
by appropriate measures of the degree to which each
of these is being realized. In an effort to achieve
a single-valued measure of societal performance, and
thus a similar measure for welfare programs, a transformation was suggested based upon some underlying
relationships among the five formulated goals and the
efficiencies with which individual goals can be obtained.

The procedures presented in Chapters 3 and 4 for
measures of societal performance from both the individualistic and the collective points of view are extremely difficult and costly to perform. As ideal
procedures, they were formulated with an emphasis not
upon ease of application but upon simplicity and consistency of concept and logic. This was in an effort
to achieve an appealing and robust methodological
framework which would provide long-range goals which
could be approached in time. It is not surprising,
therefore, that the procedures that were developed
appear almost impossible to implement. This may appear to be a weakness in our methodology, but it is

in fact one of its greatest strengths because it provides us with a clear path to follow and a yardstick
by which we can measure our progress toward the realization of the ideal.

The use of approximations can be either quite
dangerous or rather useful, depending upon the methods employed. Attitudes toward the application of
approximations vary. Consider the following situation. The law enforcement officials of a certain
municipality have received certain information from
a sampling of reported crimes and wish to use it for
deployment schemata. Even if we assume that the
sample is a true representation of the population of
reported crimes, another approximation is being made,
that is, the use of reported crimes instead of all
crimes. From recent studies done by the President's
Crime Commission, it has been estimated that, depending upon the type, reported crimes may represent as
low as 10 percent of all crimes.[1] A pessimistic law
enforcement official would argue that since in many
cases reported crimes represent only a fraction of
actual crimes, the data gathered are not only useless
but may even result in a worse deployment of manpower
than one in which pure judgment is used. An optimis-
tic officer might argue that crimes are crimes and
the information probably comes fairly close to repre-
senting the actual situation, so why not use it? A
realist, on the other hand, would argue somewhat differently. He would take the position that while one
should not use the data blindly, hoping that reported
crimes have the same characteristics as unreported
crimes, one should not completely discard the data.
Instead of prejudging the characteristics of unreported crimes, an effort should be made, if possible, to
sample this population as well, so that some data
are available on which alternative hypotheses may be
tested.

If for reasons of excessive cost, time, or other
constraints, such a sampling is unfeasible, there is
another path available. This alternative path consists of examining possible biases and attempting to
bound their magnitudes. In the absence of actual
sampling, this procedure is the best we can do. One

must be on guard lest the pessimistic attitude in-
hibit initial researches into a given area. Similarly, one must be critical of the optimist's general-
ities and research claims. The format for presenting
the approximations used in this book will be as follows. First I will present the form of actual approximations used, followed by some statements about
possible biases. I will then, in some cases, outline
more elaborate procedures which might have been used
if appropriate funds, time, and staff had been available.

USE OF STATISTICAL SAMPLING PROCEDURES

The application of statistical sampling procedures requires some thought about the attributes of
the population from which the sample is to be drawn.
The sample size should be determined by taking into
consideration the following variables: (a) cost of
sampling, (b) the sampling error as a function of
the sample size, and (c) the cost of error.

The sampling error as a function of sample size
depends upon the experimental design being employed
and the attributes of the sampled population. If,
when considering a certain attribute of the population, one finds that one can divide the population
into sets within which the elements are very homogeneous and between which differences exist, one
can gain efficiency by stratified or cluster sampling. For a complete review of such sampling techniques one may consult W. G. Cochran, M. A. Hansen
et al.. and O. Kempthorne.[2] Some forms, notably
cluster sampling, also have a beneficial effect upon
sampling costs. From the costs of sampling and the
sampling error as a function of sample size, the optimal sampling design may be obtained. The incorpo-
ration of the cost of error into the computations
will enable one to determine the optimal sample size.
This is done by increasing the sample size until the
cost of the additional sampling is equal to the cost
reduction achieved by the increased sample size
(which reduces variance, and hence the expected cost
of error).

Sampling procedures can be employed at various points in the research. While some of these will be specifically discussed later, I should like to mention a few of them at this point. First, sampling procedures can be used to select individuals from the various programs under consideration and from the population at large. Second, certain objects can be selected from the individual's operating environment and concentrated upon. Third, since the procedures may become quite involved, some of the individuals may be selected for the individualistic evaluation and others for the societal evaluation.

The rest of this chapter will be devoted to a discussion of approximation methods which may be used in the determination of the individual's utility for a program as measured by the individual welfare function and the individual's contribution to societal goals as measured by the societal welfare function.

APPROXIMATIONS TO THE INDIVIDUALISTIC
WELFARE FUNCTION

It will be remembered that the procedure presented in Chapter 3 for the determination of the value of the individualistic welfare function consisted first of identifying objects in an individual's environment for which he has a need. Once these objects were identified, a measure of the degree to which the individual's need for each of these objects was satisfied was presented. The relative importance of each of the identified objects in the individual's operating environment was then formulated. Approximations may be made in a number of ways. We shall first consider the use only of objects which are relevant in a strictly defined sense. Second, we shall consider object combinations under certain conditions. The above two approximations deal with the formulation of the objects themselves and are followed by approximation procedures to measure both the level of satisfaction and the relative importance of an object. We shall consider in the next section only the use of relevant objects.

The Use of Relevant Objects

A program undertaken by society usually has
limited objectives; for example, a "better housing"
program presumably will have little or no effect upon the diet of the participating individuals. Similarly, a program aimed at better menu planning will
have little or no effect upon housing conditions.
The procedure outlined in Chapter 3 specifies that
all objects in the operating environment should be
taken into consideration. Relevance will be defined
with respect to a given program. An object may be
considered non-relevant if any of the following is
true: (a) the program is not aimed at affecting the
level of satisfaction for a given object; (b) the
program is not aimed at affecting the relative importance of an object; (c) the program fails to affect either the level of satisfaction or the relative
importance of an object. Thus an object may be intended to be non-relevant, or it may become non-
relevant because of program failure. In either case,
I will show that there is a class of non-relevant objects which have no effect upon comparisons among
alternative programs, provided that the object is
either excluded from or included in all the alternatives, or that the program utilities have been adjusted by subtracting the change in utilities experienced by a control group. All objects other than
those which are determined to be non-relevant are
called relevant.

An operational definition of a non-relevant object will be made much simpler by first presenting
definitions of unaffected and stable objects.

Definitions of Relevance

The meaning of "unaffected" and "stable" objects
is embedded in the following procedures.

Consider an object, $\hat{O}$. Take two groups of individuals selected at random, one group about to be-
gin participating in a program and the other a control
group. Measure the level of satisfaction for each

individual with respect to $\hat{O}$. Calculate the average
level of satisfaction for each group, $\bar{n}_1(t)$ and $\bar{n}_2(t)$,
respectively. Do this again after the program is
over and obtain $\bar{n}_1(t^*)$ and $\bar{n}_2(t^*)$. Then obtain $\Delta\bar{n}_1 =$
$\bar{n}_1(t^*) - \bar{n}_1(t)$ and $\Delta\bar{n}_2 = \bar{n}_2(t^*) - \bar{n}_2(t)$. If the population values for which $\Delta\bar{n}_1$ and $\Delta\bar{n}_2$ are estimates
cannot be said to be different, then $\hat{O}$ is considered
an unaffected object with respect to the program.
(A non-parametric test such as the Mann-Whitney test
would probably be best to use in this case. If one
was willing to make the additional assumptions of
homogeneity of variance $(\sigma_1^2 = \sigma_2^2)$ and normality, a
t test could be employed.)

Repeat the procedure outlined above for unaffected objects to determine the average measures of the
relative importance of the object, $\bar{\Psi}(t)$ and $\bar{\Psi}(t^*)$.
Then compute $\Delta\bar{\Psi} = \bar{\Psi}(t^*) - \bar{\Psi}(t)$. If $\Delta\bar{\Psi}$ is not significantly different from zero, then the object is a
stable one.

A non-relevant object can now be defined as an
object which is both stable and unaffected with respect to each of the alternative programs under consideration.

One may show that whether or not a non-relevant
object is included in all the alternatives will make
no difference in the resulting values for each program, save the addition of a constant to all the
values. (It should be noted that the definition of
a non-relevant object ignores distributional properties. For example, a large change in one direction
for some people could be offset by a similarly large
change in the other direction for others. If this is
believed possible for the particular application being considered, an appropriate change in the definition must be made. Such a change would include a
test of significance for the distributions. The case
is, I feel, not the usual one.) Such an argument
would go as follows.

Consider two programs, P_1 and P_2, which serve
the same population. Let O_1 be a non-relevant object
for both programs. We can express the expected

utility of the two programs to two individuals, k and k', one from each program, as:

$$E\left\{U_k[P_1]\right\} = E\left\{U[S_k^1(t*)]\right\} - E\left\{U[S_k(t)]\right\}$$

and

$$E\left\{U_{k'}[P_2]\right\} = E\left\{U[S_{k'}^2(t*)]\right\} - E\left\{U[S_{k'}(t)]\right\} .$$

Since k' and k are drawn from the same population,

$$E\left\{U[S_k(t)]\right\} = E\left\{U[S_{k'}(t)]\right\} .$$

For simplification let us replace these by $\bar{U}(t)$.

Now $E\left\{U[S_k^1(t*)]\right\} = \dfrac{1}{N_1} \sum\limits_{k=1}^{N_1} \sum\limits_{i=1}^{m} \psi_{1ik}(t*) \, n_{ik}^1(t*)$

$$= \sum\limits_{i=1}^{m} \bar{\Psi}_{1i}(t*) \, \bar{n}_i^1(t*)$$

$$= \sum\limits_{i=2}^{m} \bar{\Psi}_{1i}(t*) \cdot \bar{n}_i^1(t*) + \bar{\Psi}_{11}(t*) \cdot \bar{n}_1^1(t*)$$

and $E\left\{U[S_k^2(t*)]\right\} = \dfrac{1}{N_2} \sum\limits_{k=1}^{N_2} \sum\limits_{i=1}^{m} \psi_{1ik}(t*) \, n_{ik}^1(t*)$

$$= \sum\limits_{i=2}^{m} \bar{\Psi}_{2i}(t*) \cdot \bar{n}_i^2(t*) + \bar{\Psi}_{21}(t*) \cdot \bar{n}_1^2(t*) .$$

Since O_1 is a non-relevant object, then

$$\bar{n}_1^1(t*) = \bar{n}_2^2(t*)$$

and

$$\bar{\Psi}_{11}(t*) = \bar{\Psi}_{21}(t*) .$$

Let us replace these by $\bar{n}_1(t*)$ and $\bar{\Psi}_1(t*)$. Now we can express the expected utilities of the two programs as

$$E\left\{U_k[P_1]\right\} = \sum\limits_{i=2}^{m} \bar{\Psi}_{1i}(t*) \cdot \bar{n}_i^1(t*) + \bar{\Psi}_1(t*) \cdot \bar{n}_1(t*) - \bar{U}(t)$$

and

$$E\left\{U_k[P_2]\right\} = \sum_{i=2}^{m} \bar{\Psi}_{2i}(t*)\cdot\bar{n}_i^2(t*) + \bar{\Psi}_1(t*)\cdot\bar{n}_1(t*) - \bar{U}(t).$$

Thus, if O_1 is included in the analysis, both of the expected utilities of the programs are altered by the addition of the quantity $\bar{\Psi}_1(t*)\cdot\bar{n}_1(t*)$, which does not affect a comparison between the two programs.

The actual determination of the relevance of an object can be performed only after the program has been implemented. It is possible, however, to esti-mate a priori which objects are non-relevant and which are not by using the results of previous studies, by running a pilot study, or by means of an educated guess. Educated guesses, however, must be made with extreme care, for there may be cases in which an ob-ject may appear to be non-relevant but is in fact relevant. The first type of approximation consists in making a list of relevant objects that are to be considered. In practice, this list is limited by the funds available, the rights of privacy of the participants, and the skill of the interviewer. The main advantage of this method of determining relevant objects, in comparison with accepting the stated aims of the program, is that more of the effects and ram-ifications of a program are taken into consideration. It is possible that an object which should be relevant is deemed non-relevant if the alternative programs have the same shortcomings as the program being con-sidered. In such cases these objects may be rein-stated if, in the opinion of the researcher, future programs that will be included in the analyses may be more effective than those currently being tested. Certainly, truly non-relevant objects cannot affect current results.

Possible Introduction of Errors

If enough time and money were available, pilot studies could be designed to investigate the proba-bility of various objects being non-relevant with respect to particular programs. There are, of course, two types of possible errors and four kinds of

situations. The first type of error is to consider
a given object non-relevant when it is in fact relevant. The object may be relevant in two ways. Either
the object was intended to be relevant or it was not.
The latter situation, that is, an object being relevant when it was not intended to be so, is more likely to occur unnoticed than an error in classifying
objects intended to be relevant. If no pilot is conducted, one can never make the error of misclassify-
ing those objects intended to be relevant when they
are, in fact, relevant. However, if a pilot is not
done, objects which were never intended to be relevant (secondary effects, backlash, etc.) but are
relevant will not be detected underline they are, by
design, included in the study to guard against this
type of error. Such precautions were taken in the
study from which our data is taken.

The second kind of error, that of calling objects relevant when in fact they are not, can also
be considered as having two components--those which
were intended to be non-relevant and those which were
intended to be relevant. If no pilot study is done,
one can never make the mistake of calling objects intended to be non-relevant, relevant. Similarly, we
would never catch those objects which were intended
to be relevant and turned out to be non-relevant.
But here the cost of error would be equal only to the
marginal cost of including these objects in the study.
By far the most important type of error is failure to
recognize objects which are relevant but were never
intended to be so. This type of error can be statistically controlled only by a pilot study or by including objects never intended to be relevant in the
study. Whether or not one runs a pilot depends upon
the costs involved. If the cost of running the pilot
study is less than the cost of obtaining additional
information during the actual study, then one should
use a pilot study. I should now like to turn to the
consideration of combinations of objects.

The Use of Object Combinations

Another desirable approximation involves the
combination of several objects. It may be worthwhile

in either of the following two situations: (1) two
or more objects are substitutable for one another,
or (2) two or more objects complement one another.
Substitutability is an attribute which is dependent
upon the property of the object being considered.
Wine, steak, and spinach are mutually substitutable
if caloric intake is the property in question but are
not substitutable under other circumstances. Steak
and tripe may be substitutable in terms of protein
content but not when taste is being considered. The
more general the property in question, the greater
the number of objects which can be considered substitutable. Consider the number of objects you would
consider substituting for each of the following objects: steak, beef, meat, entree, and food.

Complementary objects are those whose utilities
are enhanced by their simultaneous occurrence, that
is, the utility of their joint occurrence is greater
than the sum of the utilities of their individual
occurrence. Examples of complementary objects are
coffee and sugar, a desk and a chair, and matching
handbag and shoes. Complementary objects are strictly defined for a given individual. However, in general parlance two or more objects are said to be
complementary if many people concur. How many is
"many"? If one were to try to determine this number,
one could say that if the group's demand curves were
very similar, the objects were either complementary
or substitutable.

Objects which are considered to be either complementary or substitutable may be combined and re-
labeled by the class or property being considered.
In Chapter 6 such combinations of objects will be
made and the classes to which they belong will be
identified for the data used.

The effects of such object combinations upon an
analysis of alternative programs depend upon the degree to which the objects are either substitutable
or complementary. The analyses will for the most
part benefit from object combinations for two reasons.
First, the analysis is simplified by the reduction
of the number of objects or object combinations

considered. Second, a more realistic picture is
achieved by using combinations, since they account
for some of the interdependencies between objects
which would not be included in the analysis. Again,
if time and costs permitted, a pilot study to determine dependencies could be undertaken. One could
determine whether a pilot study was worthwhile by
comparing costs in a way similar to that outlined
for the determination of relevance.

Approximate Measures of the
Levels of Satisfaction

Other approximations involve deviations from the
procedures outlined in Chapter 3 for obtaining the
perceived levels of satisfaction and the value of the
states described by these levels. The procedure outlined to measure levels of satisfaction involves
identifying the number of units which saturate the individual and the number of units possessed. One approximation would be to establish a standard saturation level for each object rather than to determine
saturation levels for each individual. What effect
would this have upon the resulting measures of the
levels of satisfaction? The answer to this depends
upon the number of units selected as the saturation
level. If the standard level is very high, indeed
high enough so that everyone would be saturated by a
lesser amount, then this method of estimating the perceived levels of satisfaction would always result in
underestimates. On the other hand, suppose that no-
body would be saturated by the number of units chosen
for the standard saturation level. In this case the
procedure would result in overestimates of the levels
of satisfaction. There exists a standard saturation
level which will provide an unbiased estimate of the
level of satisfaction, and this level is equal to the
average of the individual's saturation levels. (A
proof of this may be found in Appendix B.)

Approximate Measures of the Relative
Importance of an Object

The experimental procedure outlined in Chapter
3 for determining the relative importance of various

objects to an individual is a fairly expensive one.
Cost savings could be made in a number of ways. I
will present three methods of approximation and then
discuss the various advantages and disadvantages of
each.

The first method to be considered involves sampling. Instead of experimentally determining every
individual's relative value for every object, one
could select a sample of individuals and from the results of this experiment obtain an estimate of the
group's average relative importance for an object and
use this estimate for all individuals. Another method which could be used to estimate the relative importance of the various objects is simply to ask each
individual directly to evaluate the importance of an
object to himself, say on a scale from 0-10. The
third approximation is to have the relative value of
various objects or classes of objects estimated for
each individual by an outside observer.

The first method has an advantage in that the
values obtained are known to be correct for the sample group. However, the use of a single value for
each object may give a distorted view if the group
is not homogeneous. Since the relative value of an
object depends upon the state the individual is in,
using the estimated mean value of an object for all
individuals will produce a biased result. A positive bias occurs if a pair of objects is negatively
correlated for individuals. In most cases this occurs because marginal utility is usually inversely
proportional to the amount possessed. Symbolically,
let V be the value and S be the level of satisfaction.
If S and V are negatively correlated, then $E(SV) <$
$E(S) \cdot E(V)$. E(SV) would occur if no group mean approximation were used, while

$$E(S) \cdot E(V) = \frac{1}{n} \sum_{i=1}^{n} \bar{S} \, V_i$$

would appear in an approximation using the group
mean. Hence, the approximation is always greater
or a positive bias is present.

The individual's direct evaluation of the various needs is dangerous for one important reason. This is that individuals have a need commonly known as "pride," which is manifested by the individual's distortion of the relative importance of his various other needs. This difficulty can, however, be overcome by trained and experienced interviewers; and when it is, this method becomes a very attractive one because each individual is considered separately, overcoming what may be a problem of estimating and removing bias.

The third method can be criticized on the grounds that the observer may be inadvertently attributing his values to the individual (transference) and thus introducing a bias. If care in selecting and training observers is taken, this difficulty may be overcome. At any rate, during the analysis one can test for observer effects, to see whether they are significant.

So far in this chapter I have discussed various ways of making approximations to the measures defined in Chapter 3. These approximations consist of selecting a sample of people from the programs to be evaluated, finding relevant objects and combinations of objects, and using approximate measures of both the level of satisfaction and the relative importance of the various needs. These approximations will be applied when programs are evaluated in Chapter 6.

APPROXIMATIONS TO THE SOCIETAL WELFARE FUNCTION

In Chapter 4 I introduced a measure, $\Lambda(w)$, of the degree to which the goals of society are being realized. Now I will be concerned with approximations to this societal welfare function, which can be used in evaluating the effectiveness of alternative welfare programs.

Separate measures could probably be developed for each of the services performed by society in an attempt to perform the functions listed in Chapter 4.

The difficulty, aside from purely arithmetical problems arising from the use of many measures, stems
from the fact that these measures are not independent;
for example, a better transportation system may affect the performance of education, of protection, and
of many other services. Unfortunately, no existing
single measure would by itself adequately reflect
changes in the performance of all of the societal
functions. In Chapter 2 we saw that the existing
measures (or indicants) do not adequately reflect the
true degree of the performance of even one of society's functions. This inadequacy is, however, largely the result of practical considerations rather than
of conceptual inadequacies.

Approximate Measures of the Degree to Which the Goals of Society Are Realized

The actual determination of the measures of the
degree to which societal goals $I(t)$, $M(t)$, $D(t)$,
$R(t)$, and $P(t)$ are being attained is difficult and
costly. We have therefore selected five indicants
which we feel constitute a reasonable initial attempt
at an approximation to the above measures. The degree to which these indicants reflect the actual situation is not known; nor is it likely to be known
for quite some time, since the validation procedures
which are needed involve obtaining estimates of the
measures themselves. The evaluation of the effectiveness of a specific welfare program entails obtaining the change in the degree to which the group
of participating individuals is contributing to the
realization of societal goals. After careful consideration of the nature of the available data, it
was decided that the following five indicants were
the best to use as an approximation to the societal
function:

1. the group's net contribution to the
    gross national product
2. the group's crime rate
3. the group's level of education
4. the group's level of religious and
    community participation
5. the group's level of information.

The relative weights that should be assigned to each
of these five indicants depend heavily upon the situation in which they are being employed. Clearly,
not all welfare programs are broadly based enough to
affect all of the above indicants. Some judgment
must be employed to determine which of the indicants
are relevant in a particular case, and what their
relative importance is. The sensitivity of the outcome to the weights assigned could then be determined.

The increase in the group's contribution to
gross national product is included to provide an indication of the effect of the program upon the functions
of manufacturing, distribution, and provision. The
group's crime rate is included for the purpose of re-
flecting the amount of protection being provided.
The group's level of education and level of information serve as indicators of increases in distribution
of knowledge. Finally, changes in the group's level
of religious and community participation serve as an
indication of the program's effect upon the level of
inspiration.

Definitions of the Approximate Measures
of Participation

A group's net contribution to the gross national
product is the sum of the net contributions of the
individuals in the group. An individual's net contribution will be considered to be the monetary equivalent of the sum total of the goods he produces and
the services he performs, minus the monetary equivalent of the goods and services he receives from welfare agencies (transfer payments). The group's crime
rate would be the number of index crimes that its
members have committed, divided by the average for
the population for a suitable period of time. The
level of education would be simply the average years
of formal schooling or equivalent achievement, while
the level of religious and community participation
would be the average number of hours devoted to such
activities per time period. Finally, the level of
information is measured by the average number and degree of usage of sources of information (newspapers,
books, radio, television) that are available in a
given time period.

While each of these measures is rather crude,
I do not feel that more sophisticated techniques are
called for as yet, since these will probably be sufficient to differentiate among several alternative
groups. For example, if one owns two overcoats, a
winter one and a fall one, any information beyond
whether or not it is cold enough for the winter overcoat or warm enough for no overcoat is of no value.
Here the added cost of using more sophisticated techniques of measuring would, I fear, yield information
of only marginal value.

A danger exists in that most of the above measures would not be lagged in time, that is, that a
period of time would elapse between the action of
the program and the resulting change in the above
measures. If this is not taken into account, a program might be killed before its true effects were
known. It may become possible to develop attitude
measures sophisticated enough to act as predictors
of changes in the long-term measures, thus reducing
the time needed to determine the change in the measures brought about by the program. Until such measures are developed, we must use the best that are
currently available.

Measurement of Error Caused by Approximations

Two types of approximations have been presented
for the societal function. The first was more conceptual in nature and represented an approach rather
than an estimate of a measure. Such an approximation
can be truly validated only by testing the logical
consistency of its development. The ultimate acceptance of this development of a societal welfare function, indicated by its use in evaluating the effectiveness of welfare programs, would, therefore, be a
de facto validation of this approximation. The other
type of approximation can be tested in a way similar
to the procedures discussed in the earlier parts of
this chapter. Take, for example, the use of the number of index crimes the individuals in the group committed, divided by the average number for the population, as an approximate measure of the group's crime
rate, or the use of the years of school or equivalent

as an approximation of the level of education. How
good are these approximations? As approximations or
indicants they should be highly correlated with a
measure of educational level or crime rate. This
calls for a generally accepted measure to use as a
yardstick. Once such a measure is found, a pilot
study could be run to determine the "goodness" of the
approximation. With regard to the selection of approximate measures, I feel that if in fact a bias
does exist, it is constant over the groups selected
from various parts of the population and hence will
have no effect upon the results.

Combining the Indicants into a
Unidimensional Measure

We now have five approximate measures of the
degree to which a group of individuals contributes
to the performance of society's functions. A welfare
program can be evaluated by the change it produces
in each of these measures. It would be helpful if
we could combine these five approximate measures into
one, as was done with the ideal measures in Chapter
4, by relating them to individual achievement. In
an actual application it is unlikely that all of these
measures will be relevant. Nevertheless, alternative
programs which are relevant to different measures
must be capable of being compared.

Thus a method of transforming the approximate
measures of $I(t)$, $M(t)$, $D(t)$, $R(t)$, and $P(t)$ into an
approximation to $\Lambda(w)$ must be provided. As an approximation to η, the function which weights the
various measures of societal goals, I propose to use
estimates of $U_k(P_j)$ resulting from the individualistic
function to estimate η, instead of V_j. The procedure
is as follows:

Let $\hat{\eta}$ be the estimate of η which consists of the
five weights $\eta_1, \ldots, \eta_5$. Let $I_k'(t)$, $M_k'(t)$, $D_k'(t)$,
$R_k'(t)$, and $P_k'(t)$ represent the approximations to the
measures for the kth individual. Let

$$U_k(p) = \hat{\eta}(I_k'(t), M_k'(t), D_k'(t), R_k'(t), P_k'(t),$$

where $\hat{\eta}$ is found by performing a least-squares regression analysis.

If the contribution of a program is not significantly different from zero for any of the measures,
that measure can, of course, be eliminated from this
combinatorial procedure.

The actual application of these approximations
will be presented in Chapter 6. They will be explicitly defined in terms of the available data. The
sensitivity of the results of a comparison among the
alternative programs involved to the weighting function will also be discussed.

NOTES

1.   President's Commission on Law Enforcement
and Administration of Justice, The Challenge of Crime
in a Free Society (Washington, D.C.:   Government
Printing Office, 1967).

2.   W. G. Cochran, Sampling Techniques (New York:
J. Wiley and Sons, 1953); M. A. Hansen, W. N. Hurwitz,
and W. A. Madow, Sample Survey Methods and Theory
(New York: J. Wiley and Sons, 1953); O. Kempthorne,
The Design and Analysis of Experiments (New York:
J. Wiley and Sons, 1952).

CHAPTER **6** ANALYSIS OF THE
EFFECTIVENESS OF
ACTUAL WELFARE
PROGRAMS, USING
BOTH THE INDIVID-
UALISTIC AND
SOCIETAL FUNCTIONS

REVIEW OF DATA REQUIREMENTS

Before discussing the specific data that were
used, let me briefly review what is needed for the
construction of both functions, taking the individualistic function first. It will be remembered that
the utility of a program can be thought of as the
sum of the weighted levels of satisfaction the individual experiences with respect to the objects in
his operating environment. The weights that are employed represent the relative importance of the objects to the individual. One of the approximations
that was introduced in Chapter 5 was the use of a
standard saturation level instead of the individual's
own level. The standard saturation levels which are
used in this analysis were selected by experts in
the field of social work rather than by the expensive
procedure outlined in Chapter 5. It was felt that
expert judgment would be adequate for the purposes
of this analysis because the population seemed quite
homogeneous as far as the objects needed were concerned. Similarly, I have chosen to use expert judgments as the basis for the calculations of the
relative importance of the various objects.

In Chapter 5 some approximations to the societal
welfare function were presented. These approximations were in the form of measures of the contributions that individuals make to the successful performance of the functions which are undertaken by society.

The five measures selected in Chapter 5 were:

1. the group's net contribution to the
   gross national product
2. the group's crime rate
3. the group's level of education
4. the group's level of religious and
   community participation
5. the group's level of information.

Since the studies we will be using in the evaluation
have all taken place in the past, the question is
merely how we can best approximate these measures
from the data already obtained.

The remainder of this chapter will review the
data-gathering experiment and the use of these data
in the analysis. The results of the analysis will
then be presented and discussed. (The actual computations will be presented in Appendix D.)

THE DATA GATHERING EXPERIMENT

The Experimental Population

A data-gathering experiment was conducted by the
Research Center of the School of Social Work of the
University of Pennsylvania during the period 1965-66,
under the direction of Dr. Julius J. Jahn, for the
Philadelphia Child Welfare Project (PCWP). This experiment was a part of the initial planning phase of
the project, whose purpose was to provide initial
ideas from which future studies would be conducted by
the University Research Center. The details can be
found in Jahn and Gelin.[1]

The main purpose of this initial study was to
provide a basis for the statistical selection of variables which seem to provide logical criteria with
which the effectiveness of the programs can be measured. The next phase, currently being undertaken,
is to repeat the experiment concentrating upon col-
lecting those variables selected after the first phase
so that changes in these criteria can be measured.

Background material and related problems can be found in Lewis and Jahn, Blenker and Jahn, Bishop and Lewis, and Jahn.[2] I will be specifically concerned here only with the data-gathering phase of this study; the actual analysis and general conception may be found in the above works.

The population that was sampled consisted of individuals living in the city of Philadelphia. These are divided into seven strata, which can be found in Table 1. It should be noted that groups A1 and A2 are mutually exclusive, as are B1, B2, B3, B4, and B5, but that a member of one of the A groups might be included in one of the B groups because of the difference in the time periods involved.

Selection of the Sample

Within each of the agency strata (A1, A2, B1, B2, and B3) the samples were obtained by listing all persons who were in these groups on the date on which the samples were selected. Simple random samples were then drawn from these lists. The sampling rates were determined so as to obtain about 30 families in each of the seven strata. Cost considerations necessitated the reduction of the sample selected from stratum B1 by half.

For the non-agency groups, B4 and B5, the sampling method involved, first, a random selection of city blocks listed in the 1960 U.S. census, then listing dwelling units within the specified blocks. A random selection of dwelling units from this list was made, followed by a random selection of households. From the selected households, one adult member was pre-designated for interviewing. The female parent was preferred. The second choice was the male of the household. For children in the household, one from each of the age groups 12-18 and under 12 was to be randomly selected. The selection of the blocks differed slightly between B4 and B5. For B4, the blocks were selected by first accumulating lists of all families registered in the local Social Service Exchange. (All persons accepted for service at member organizations are registered. Virtually all important sources

TABLE 1

The Stratification of the Population Used in
the Study of the Effectiveness of
Philadelphia Child Welfare
Programs

Stratum	Description of Stratum
A1	Former Clients of Intensive Service. Members of families included in the Intensive Service Project (ISP) of the Philadelphia Society to Protect Children (PSPC). Service was rendered during the years 1959-62.
A2	Former Clients of Standard Service. Members of families who received service from PSPC but did not participate in ISP.
B1	Current Clients of Standard Service. Members of families who "currently" (during the period 1965-66) had been accepted by PSPC for service.
B2	Rejected Referrals of Standard Service. Members of families referred to PSPC but not accepted for service during time period defined for Group B1.
B3	Current Clients of Other Agencies. Members of families accepted for service by other agencies. In this case the other agency was Youth Service, Inc. (YS).
B4	Neighbors. Members of families not receiving service whose residence is in the same block as families in Groups B1, B2, and B3.
B5	General Population. Non-clients, non-neighbors.

Source: H. Lewis et al., Designing More Effective Protective Services (Philadelphia: Research Center, School of Social Work, University of Pennsylvania, 1967), pp. 83-85.

78

of aid are members of the Social Service Exchange.)
Next a 1 percent sample was selected and non-
Philadelphia residents were excluded. A sub-sample
of nine families was randomly selected, and the blocks
in which they resided were used. For B5, the blocks
were selected directly from the census listing, adjusted for vacant blocks. The actual sample sizes
are entered in Table 2.

TABLE 2

Sample Sizes for the Strata

Stratum	Sample
A1 Intensive (Former)	28 Families
A2 Standard (Former)	33 Families
B1 Standard (Current)	14 Families
B2 Rejected	25 Families
B3 Other Agency	7 Adults
	29 Older Children
B4 Neighbors	23 Dwellings
B5 Block Sample	26 Dwellings

Source: H. Lewis et al., Designing More Effective
         Protective Services (Philadelphia: Re-
         Search Center, School of Social Work, Uni-
         versity of Pennsylvania, 1967), p. 85.

Interviewing Procedures

     Interviewers were selected from persons with
some training and experience in social work who had
clients living in the areas covered by the survey.
Two weeks of training were given to all interviewers.
Interviews were carried out during the period between
February and May, 1966. The interviewers were in-
structed to attempt to contact the sample families
or persons on at least three separate occasions before classifying the research schedule (questionnaire)
as incomplete. Table 3 shows the number completed
in each stratum, and Table 4 shows the distribution
of reasons for the non-completed interviews.

TABLE 3

Percentage and Number of Research
Questionnaires, by Stratum

Stratum	No. Assigned	No. Completed	% Completed
A1	28	11	39
A2	33	12	36
B1	14	7	50
B2	25	5	20
B3	29	28	97
	7	6	86
B4	23	9	39
B5	26	16	62

Source: H. Lewis et al., Designing More Effective Protective Services (Philadelphia: Research Center,
School of Social Work, University of Pennsylvania
1967), p. 88.

TABLE 4

Distribution of Reasons for Non-Completed
Questionnaires

Stratum	Not Located	Refusal	Other
A1	17	--	--
A2	20	--	1
B1	6	1	--
B2	12	4	4
B3	1	--	--
	1		
B4	--	14	--
B5	--	10	--

Source: H. Lewis et al., Designing More Effective Protective Services (Philadelphia: Research Center,
School of Social Work, University of Pennsylvania,
1967), p. 89.

In any statistical survey or study, observations sometimes cannot be made; this may introduce bias(es) into the analyses. In this particular case we are dealing with human subjects who are still afforded the right to refuse to be observed. Refusals accounted for less than 10 percent of non-completed questionnaires for those individuals or families taking part in some welfare program and for 100 percent of the non-completed questionnaires for those not participating in a program. The vast majority of non-completed questionnaires for participating individuals resulted from failure to locate them. It would have been desirable to resample refusals and locate some of those previously unlocatable, but realistically this was not possible. Thus, we must try to analyze possible biases which may occur, since we cannot measure them. For participating individuals, refusals really were not a problem because of their small number and because 80 percent of refusals came from rejected applicants, who naturally would be disinclined to participate in the study. The individuals who could not be located are more likely to be the cause of bias. They may be unlocatable because their situation has either improved or worsened, resulting in their either moving voluntarily or being forced to move. It is interesting to note that almost the same percentage were not located from each of the former programs. Actually, there appears no reason why non-completed questionnaires from any one of the groups should be different from any other non-completed ones. If any bias exists, it would seem to be fairly consistent over groups. Therefore, it would have no major effect upon the comparisons.

The Questionnaire*

The questionnaire was 68 pages long and was subdivided into the following 10 sections:

1. general information
2. housing

─────────────

*Sections of the questionnaire that are relevant to this book are presented in Appendix C.

3. occupation
4. financial situation
5. public health
6. adjustment
7. interpersonal relations
8. activities and interests
9. respondent's comments
10. interviewer's analysis.

Taking each in turn, I will briefly summarize the
information sought in each of the sections.

The general information section aimed at getting
background data on the individual which could be used
to classify him by such attributes as age, sex, place
of birth, and level of education. The housing section asked for information relating to the type of
dwelling, furniture and appliances possessed, and
characteristics of dwellings in the neighborhood. The
occupation section dealt with the number of jobs held
during the individual's career and his attitudes toward these jobs.

Included in the financial section were questions
relating to the individual's dependents, to the distribution of his expenses, and to the sources of his
income. The section on physical health dealt with
both physical and mental illnesses or defects of the
individual and the aid and treatment he received.
The section on adjustment aimed at obtaining. information concerning the individual's attitudes about himself in relation to other individuals. The interpersonal relations section sought information about
the number and extent of relationships the individual
had with other persons, both within and outside his
own family.

The section on activities and interests aimed
at getting information pertaining to the type, number,
and extent of activities the individual performed,
with emphasis upon the religious, fraternal, social,
and professional organizations of which the individual was a member. The comment section dealt with any
special problems, views, or attitudes the individual
might want to express concerning his own situation,

the welfare agency, or the interview itself. This
section was not coded, nor was the information trans-
ferred to IBM cards.

The last section gave the interviewer the opportunity to state the conditions influencing the interview and his opinions concerning the state of the
respondent. The interviews were classified by subject and by interviewee, since these were not necessarily the same person. Adults were asked to respond
for the older child if he was not present and for the
younger child in all cases. Adults always answered
for themselves. The sections on housing, occupation,
and finance applied only to adults. Younger children
were not used in the analyses.

USE OF THE DATA FOR THE INDIVIDUALISTIC
WELFARE FUNCTION

For the purposes of analysis the four object
sets that were considered to be relevant were selected and the "units" defined. (The "objects" in each
set were considered to be similar enough in function
to be thought of as units belonging to a class. Thus,
we will simply refer to each set as an object and
each object as a unit.) Each unit was chosen from
the questions contained in the questionnaire. The
four sets of objects were

1. household possessions
2. health
3. self-image
4. interpersonal relations.

The unit composition of each of these objects may be
found in Appendix C.

The relative importance of each of these objects
is approximated from some judgments of the interviewer
concerning the individual's

1. material circumstances
2. self-acceptance and
    responsibility

3. physical and emotional health
4. effectiveness in social living.

It is assumed that the "better off" the individual
is judged to be in each of these areas, relative to
the other areas, the lower the level of importance
that should be attached to the corresponding object.
(This assumption can be stated symbolically as
$V_i^{-1}(t) \sim n_i(t)$. A discussion of the relationship between the relative importance of an object and the
level of satisfaction can be found in Chapter 3.) It
is recognized that this assumption may be objected to
on the grounds that individuals may value satisfaction with respect to one or more of these objects regardless of the current state of affairs. On the
other hand, I feel that the above objection is realistic only if the need for objects other than those
highly valued has reached an acceptable level, and
that this is not the case with most welfare recipients.
(If the assumption is still distasteful, other conclusions may be drawn from the data and the sensitivity of the results calculated.)

Results Obtained Using the
Individualistic Function

The results of the application of the individualistic function can be summarized in one value, the
mean of the distribution of $U_k(P_j)$ for each program.
Mean values for the various alternative programs are
presented in Table 5. Whether or not differences between programs are significant can be determined by
an appropriate test of significance. Normally one
would use a parametric test such as the t test. Even
though this test is quite robust with regard to its
underlying assumptions (independence, normality, and
equality of variance), the normality assumption may
not be justifiable in this case. A test for normality may be employed to determine whether or not the
assumption holds.

One could use the non-parametric Kolmogorov-
Smirnov test. The null hypothesis would be that the
distribution is normal with known mean and variance,
and failure to reject this hypothesis would be

TABLE 5

Summary of Results Obtained by the Application of the Individualistic
Function in Terms of the Mean Values of Program Utilities

Program	Children		Adults		Combined	
	Sample Size	Mean	Sample Size	Mean	Sample Size	Mean
Current Standard Service, B1	3	.73	6	.67	9	.71
Rejected Referrals, B2	--	---	4	.66	4	.66
Current Other Agencies, B3	28	.68	6	.69	34	.68
Neighbors, B4	1	.70	9	.73	10	.73
Other Residents, B5	4	.76	15	.69	19	.70
Former Intensive Service, A1	7	.71	11	.72	18	.72
Former Standard Service, A2	7	.75	11	.66	18	.69

Source: Compiled by author.

construed as being no evidence that such an assumption was unwarranted. Such tests were made on the data resulting from the individualistic function, and the null hypothesis that the distributions were normal failed to be rejected. Variances of these distributions are presented in Table 6.

TABLE 6

Variances of Distributions of Program Utilities
Obtained by the Individualistic Function

| Program | Children | | Adults | |
	Sample Size	Variance	Sample Size	Variance
B1	3	.002	6	.01
B2	--	----	4	.007
B3	28	.006	6	.003
B4	--	----	9	.007
B5	4	.004	15	.007
A1	7	.01	11	.009
A2	7	.01	11	.01

Source: Compiled by author.

Before a t test can be run to make pairwise comparisons of the results, F tests should be performed to see whether the variances concerned are not significantly different, since this is an assumption of the t test. Table 7 presents the results of F tests performed on the pairs of variances we wished to test. Since in each case the table values exceeded the computed values, no evidence of significant differences was found. With this accomplished, some comparisons between means were made; these results are presented in Table 8. The levels at which they may be said to be significant are also given. The t values were computed by the following formula, using the variance of a difference between the two means from independent samples employing estimated variances:

TABLE 7

Tests for Equality of Variances of Distributions of Program Utilities

Group 1	Group 2	Sample Size	Calculated F Ratio	F Table $\alpha = .01$
A1 (Adults)	A2 (Adults)	(11, 11)	1.10	4.85
B1 (Children)	B3 (Children)	(3, 28)	3.00	26.60
A2 (Children)	B3 (Children)	(7, 28)	1.66	3.59
A1 (Children)	B3 (Children)	(7, 28)	1.66	3.59
A1 (Adults)	B3 (Adults)	(11, 6)	3.00	10.05
A1 (Adults)	B1 (Adults)	(11, 6)	1.10	10.05
A1 (Adults)	B2 (Adults)	(11, 4)	1.30	27.23

Source: Compiled by author.

TABLE 8

Some Comparisons Between Program Means

Higher Mean	Lower Mean	Sample Size	Difference in Means	Significance Level
A1 (Adults)	A2 (Adults)	(11, 11)	.08	.05
B1 (Children)	B3 (Children)	(3, 28)	.10	.05
A2 (Children)	B3 (Children)	(7, 28)	.07	.05
A1 (Children)	B3 (Children)	(7, 28)	.05	.10
A1 (Adults)	B3 (Adults)	(11, 6)	.03	.05
A1 (Adults)	B1 (Adults)	(11, 6)	.05	.30
A1 (Adults)	B2 (Adults)	(11, 4)	.06	.20

Source: Compiled by author.

88

$$t = \frac{|\bar{x}_1 - \bar{x}_2|}{s \sqrt{1/n_1 + 1/n_2}},$$

where

$$s^2 = \frac{(n_1 - 1) \; s_1^2 + (n_2 - 1) \; s_2^2}{n_1 + n_2 - 2}.$$

For those who are still dubious about the normality assumption, a non-parametric test, the Mann-Whitney U test, was performed. Those comparisons between groups with relatively large sample sizes were also found to be significant at the following levels:

        B1 (children) vs. B3 (children)   .025
        A2 (children) vs. B3 (children)   .05
        A1 (children) vs. B3 (children)   .10

These results show that the intensive program was significantly better than the standard one and that the PCWP programs were significantly better than those of the other agency as measured by the individualistic welfare function. Computations of the levels of satisfaction can be found in Appendix D. We will now turn our attention to the application of the societal welfare function.

USE OF THE DATA FOR THE SOCIETAL WELFARE FUNCTION

In the analysis of the welfare programs under consideration, data was available to estimate the individual's (1) net contribution to the gross national product, (2) crime rate, (3) level of education, (4) level of religious and community participation, (5) level of information.

A complete description of the construction of these measures may be found in Appendix C. I will present below a rough description of each of these measures.

Net contribution to gross national product was
calculated by subtracting from earned income any aid
received, including welfare payments, medical assistance, and unemployment benefits. Crime rate contained
only convictions. Checks were made with appropriate
authorities. Level of education was obtained from
the total years of formal schooling. Level of religious and community participation was obtained by the
scope and extent of the individual's activities in
church or secular organizations. Level of information was obtained by investigating the number of activities in which the individual participated in
which information is normally transmitted.

Results Obtained Using the Societal Function

The results obtained using the societal welfare
function were tested in the same manner as those that
were obtained using the individualistic function.
(Composition of the resulting scores can be found in
Appendix C.) First, each set of pairs of strata within each of the five component measures was tested for
significance using a t test (if the results are not
significant, they would also be such using the Mann-
Whitney), with only some pairs within the community
participation turning out to be significant. This
was not surprising, since these particular programs
were not aimed at, nor could they have been expected
to have an effect upon, the other measures. In the
tables below, the mean values for each stratum are
presented (Table 9) with their variances (Table 10).
F tests are given in Table 11, and comparisons between alternatives are summarized in Table 12. It is
most interesting to note that all of the comparisons
(save one) favor the same group that the individualistic welfare function does.

INTERPRETATION OF THE RESULTS

The results obtained from the application of both
the individualistic and societal welfare functions
will be discussed here in the specific context of the
programs involved. More general inferences will be
reserved for Chapter 7.

TABLE 9

Mean Values for Measure of Religious and
Community Participation

Program	Children		Adult		Combined**	
(Strata)	Sample Size	Mean	Sample Size	Mean	Sample Size	Mean
B1	3	25	6	11	9	17
B2	--	--	4	5*	4	5
B3	28	12	6	7	34	15
B4	--	--	9	7	10	7
B5	4	12	15	11	19	12
A1	7	15	11	18	19	18
A2	7	11	11	7	18	10

*Adjusted by deletion of extreme value equal to 101.
**Adjusted by addition of mean group-value scores for parti-
cipation in elections to children's scores.

Source: Compiled by author.

TABLE 10

Variance of Distribution of Values for Religious
and Community Participation

Program	Children		Adults	
(Strata)	Sample Size	Variance	Sample Size	Variance
B1	3	143	6	126
B2	--	---	4	0
B3	28	54	6	49
B4	--	---	9	46
B5	4	109	15	105
A1	7	80	11	171
A2	7	157	11	57

Source: Compiled by author.

TABLE 11

Tests for Equality of Variances of Distribution of Religious
and Community Participation

Group 1	Group 2	Sample Size	F Ratio	F Table α = .01
A1 (Adults)	A2 (Adults)	(11, 11)	3.00	4.85
B1 (Children)	B3 (Children)	(3, 28)	2.65	5.49
A2 (Children)	B3 (Children)	(7, 28)	2.90	3.56
A1 (Children)	B3 (Children)	(7, 28)	1.46	3.56
A1 (Adults)	B3 (Adults)	(11, 6)	3.50	10.05
A1 (Adults)	B1 (Adults)	(11, 6)	1.35	10.05
A1 (Adults)	B2 (Adults)	(11, 4)	0*	

*B2 had no variance, since all observations were the same.

Source: Compiled by author.

TABLE 12

Comparison of Mean Values of Religious and Community Participation

Higher Mean	Lower Mean	Sample Size	Difference in Mean	Significance Level
A1 (Adults)	A2 (Adults)	(11, 11)	11	.05
B1 (Children)	B3 (Children)	(3, 28)	13	.01
B3* (Children)	A2 (Children)	(28, 7)	1	N.S.
A1 (Children)	B3 (Children)	(7, 28)	3	.30
A1 (Adults)	B3 (Adults)	(11, 6)	11	.05
A1 (Adults)	B1 (Adults)	(11, 6)	7	.30
A1 (Adults)	B2 (Adults)	(11, 4)	13	.05

*In reverse order from Table 5, but not significant.

Source: Compiled by author.

It should be noted that while the theory developed in the first part of the book calls for a
social action or program to be evaluated by the col-
lection of the appropriate data at two points in
time, the data used in this analysis were collected
during a single period of time. These data, however,
can still be employed, since the groups of individuals who fall into the former-client groups can be
said to be from the same population as the individuals in current service groups; that is, the only
difference between these individuals is their stage
of completion in a welfare program. Thus, one could
say that the current clients represent the former
clients before they entered their program. All the
programs under consideration were aimed primarily at
effecting a change in the individual's dealings with
his family unit and society in general. The fact
that the application of the societal function resulted in no significant differences between client
groups, whether current or former, in the areas of
contribution to gross national product, education
level, and crime rate supports the proposition that
they came from essentially the same population--which
in turn supports the use of the data in this manner.

Seven pairs of groups of individuals were found
to be significantly different when compared using
the functions developed. I should like to consider
each of these comparisons and suggest how they may
be interpreted.

First, adults in groups A1 and A2 were compared.
Group A1 consisted of former clients of intensive
service at PSPC, while group A2 consisted of former
clients of the standard program. The individuals
participating in the intensive program showed a significantly higher set of values for both the individualistic and societal welfare functions. It would
seem reasonable to conclude that the intensive program did more for the individuals who participated
and did more for society at large by enhancing this
group's participation in the community than did the
standard program.

The second comparison was made between children
in groups B1 and B3. The children in group B1 were

members of families who were current clients of the
standard PSPC program, while the children in group
B3 were members of families currently receiving aid
from YS. The children who were in the PSPC program
received significantly higher scores using both
functions. One could conclude that PSPC was doing
a better job in aiding these children.

Next a comparison was made between children
belonging to groups A2 and B3. These were members
of families who were former clients of the standard
PSPC program and members of families who were current
clients of YS, respectively. The children from PSPC
received significantly higher scores when the individualistic function was used, while the children
from YS received higher--although not significantly
higher--scores when the societal function was used.
These results seem to indicate that the children of
families who have completed the standard program were
in a better position than those currently in the YS
program. The results obtained by the application of
the societal function could indicate that the increase in societal contribution experienced while in
the program was not a lasting one. It does, however,
raise questions which can be answered only by a further investigation of the long-range effects of the
programs.

Next a comparison was made between both adults
and children belonging to groups A1 and B3. Both
comparisons resulted in finding scores obtained by
the individuals in group A1 to be significantly higher than those obtained by individuals in group B3
for both the individualistic and societal functions.
Group A1 were former clients of the PSPC intensive
program, and group B3 were current clients of YS.
These results, when contrasted with those obtained
for groups A2 and B3, seem to indicate that the intensive program's effects may last longer than the
standard program's effects.

The last comparisons were made between adults
in groups A1 and B1, former clients of intensive
service and current clients of standard service, and
between A1 and B2, former intensive versus rejected
referrals to PSPC. As would be expected, group A1

was found to be significantly higher on both functions than either B1 or B3.

The sum total of these results would indicate the success of the PSPC programs in aiding the individuals as well as society at large.

The next, and concluding, chapter will cast these results in a broader light, that of their support of the desirability and feasibility of employing the methodology developed in this book as an effective means of evaluation of social services.

NOTES

1. J. J. Jahn and B. A. Gelin, Philadelphia Child Welfare Project: Research Design for Phase I, 1965-66 (Philadelphia: Research Center, School of Social Work, University of Pennsylvania, 1966).

2. J. J. Jahn and H. Lewis, Intervening in the Recurrent Cycle of Neglect and Abuse of Children After Protective Service (Philadelphia: School of Social Work, University of Pennsylvania, 1964). (Mimeographed); J. J. Jahn and M. Blenkner, Serving the Aging, Methodological Supplement--Part 1--Experimental Design and Statistical Tests of Hypotheses (New York: Community Service Society of New York, 1964); H. Lewis and J. A. Bishop, Plan for Alternative Services--Part 1 (Philadelphia: School of Social Work, University of Pennsylvania, 1966). (Mimeographed); J. J. Jahn, The Utilization, Cost and Effectiveness of "Anti-Poverty Programs" (Philadelphia: School of Social Work, University of Pennsylvania, 1965). (Mimeographed.)

CHAPTER **7** SUMMARY AND
CONCLUSIONS

At this point it is desirable to summarize what
has been accomplished and, perhaps more important,
what has not been accomplished. In reviewing the
contents of this book, I will try to put the parts
in perspective rather than merely to furnish brief
chapter summaries.

Perhaps the major innovation was the recognition
that two measures of performance should be constructed: one from a societal point of view and one from
an individualistic perspective. In a sense these two
perspectives, used together, may replace the more
traditional cost-benefit approach. I do not mean to
imply that "cost" corresponds to the societal point
of view and "benefit" to the individualistic point
of view or vice versa, but that it is a new dichotomy
and perhaps a more fruitful one. It would certainly
reshape current approaches to the problem of evaluating social services by providing a fresh perspective to replace an approach essentially borrowed from
classical economics.

In essence, the procedure presented for evaluation of social services from each viewpoint consisted
of three basic stages. In the first stage, the fundamental goals and objectives were presented, and in
the second stage these statements were made operational by providing measures of the degree to which each
of the goals is being realized at any given point in
time. The third stage took the ideal formulation of
measures and attempted to find approximations which
can be employed in specific instances. The procedure
must be employed as a whole. That is, the third
stage, the application of the measures to specific

programs through the use of approximations, would be
of little value by itself. This is because it must
be related to the first and second stages of the investigation of the value of the approximation procedures employed. If this relationship is ignored,
no advance over the current technology in social work
will be made. Each approximation procedure's value
is actually a valid study in itself. This brings us
to one of the things not even attempted by this
study, an investigation of the effectiveness or accuracy of the indicants used in the specific case of
the child welfare programs reviewed. I feel, however,
that this can be effectively done only if the general
approach to societal evaluation presented here becomes
accepted and is employed. Only then will there be
a sufficient amount of data and variety of circumstances to permit a thorough investigation of currently used approximation procedures.

I should like to present some rather general
remarks concerning the specific results obtained in
Chapter 6 when the evaluation procedure was applied
to several specific programs, specifically about their
interpretation in light of Kenneth Arrow's impossi-
bility theorem. The theorem is stated as follows:

> If we exclude the possibility of inter-
> personal comparisons of utility, then
> the only methods of passing from indi-
> vidual tastes to social preferences
> which will be satisfactory and which
> will be defined for a wide range of
> sets of individual orderings are either
> imposed or dictatorial.*

From the results presented in Chapter 6 there
is a preliminary indication that the individualistic
welfare function and the societal welfare function
derived from a statement of the meta-goals of a democratic society may tend to produce similar results.

---

*K. Arrow, Social Choice and Individual Values
(New York: J. Wiley and Sons, 1951), p. 59.

The individualistic function employs interpersonal utilities, while the societal function does not. The development of a social welfare function from meta-goals results in what Arrow calls an imposed function. Our results may be quite far-reaching in the sense that they suggest the possibility of finding empirical evidence which can be used to map an individualistic function onto a societal function, that is, to provide a correspondence between the two. This also opens the way for the development of an operational measure of the degree to which a state or form of government is authoritarian. The development of the individualistic and societal functions was intended to present two extreme views, as well as differently constructed measures of the effectiveness of social services. The fact that the results of the societal welfare function derived from a statement of democratic meta-goals seems to converge to the results obtained by the individualistic welfare function not only supports the validity of the methodology presented in this book but also sets up one of the extremes on a possible scale of authoritarianism. For example, let the coefficient of correlation between the results obtained by the two functions be a measure of authoritarianism. When the two tend to coincide, as they do in this case, the coefficient would tend toward +1. When they are opposed, the coefficient would tend toward -1. The effectiveness of the state could then be expressed in terms of the coefficient of determination: the larger this coefficient, the stronger or more effective the control of the state. While this is mere speculation and will continue to be so for a long time, the fact that such speculation seems worth investigating can be considered an important by-product of this study.

Even if custom did not require a modest note on the shortcomings of this research, they are far too important to dismiss without comment.

No initial attempt at something as important and difficult as the development of a methodology for the evaluation of social services can be expected to yield a finished product. Besides the obvious necessity for more data, particularly of a nature which

will enable us to estimate directly some of the measures proposed, another area of research would enable
us to advance toward an improved methodology. This
would involve an investigation of the consequences
of the use of societal functions based upon a number
of alternative formulations of societal meta-goals.
It is my hope that this work will serve as a founda-
tion from which others may continue with this effort
in developing a framework within which social programs
can be evaluated and social structures analyzed.

APPENDIXES

APPENDIX   A   EXPLANATION AND
APPLICATION OF
THE CHURCHMAN-
ACKOFF MEASURE
OF UTILITY

The Churchman-Ackoff approximate measure of
value or utility, unlike the von Neumann-Morgenstern
and the Davidson-Siegel-Suppes measures, does not
make any assumptions about subjective probability,
maximization of expected value, or the value of a
gamble. First I will state the assumptions underlying this method, and then I will present a simple
example to demonstrate its application.

There are three assumptions underlying this
method of obtaining utility:

1. To each outcome in a situation consisting
of a set of outcomes, there corresponds a real non-
negative number to be considered as a measure of the
true utility of the outcome in <u>that</u> situation.

2. If one outcome is more important to the individual than another, the utility which corresponds
to the more important outcome will be greater than
the utility which corresponds to the less important
outcome.

3. The simultaneous attainment of two outcomes
will have a utility equal to the sum of the utilities
corresponding to each of the two outcomes.

I will demonstrate this method by presenting an
example involving four outcomes. Let these four outcomes be the receipt of the following four objects:
hot lunch, taxi ride, movie ticket, and phonograph
record.

Step 1

Have the individual assign a real, non-negative number to each of these outcomes (objects) which reflects his relative value for it. Suppose the values assigned are 3, 2, 5, and 6, respectively.

Step 2

Assign labels O_1, O_2, O_3, O_4 to values of the objects in the descending order of value. Thus O_1 would be the value of the receipt of the record, O_2 would be the value of the receipt of the ticket, O_3 would be the value of the receipt of the hot lunch, and O_4 would be the value of the receipt of the taxi ride.

Step 3

Ask if O_1 is preferred to the simultaneous occurrence of O_2, O_3, and O_4. If not, then ask if O_1 is preferred to the simultaneous occurrence of O_2 and O_3. Suppose O_1 was not preferred to the simultaneous occurrence of O_2, O_3, and O_4 ($O_1 < O_2 + O_3 + O_4$) but was preferred to the simultaneous occurrence of O_2 and O_3 ($O_1 > O_2 + O_3$).

Step 4

Ask if O_2 is preferred to the simultaneous occurrence of O_3 and O_4. Suppose O_2 is not prefered to the simultaneous occurrence of O_3 and O_4 ($O_2 < O_3 + O_4$).

Step 5

From the individual's responses, determine whether the values assigned in Step 1 are consistent, as follows:

From Steps 3 and 4 we know that

$$O_1 < O_2 + O_3 + O_4$$
$$O_1 > O_2 + O_3$$
$$O_2 < O_3 + O_4.$$

Substituting values from Step 1:

$$6 < 5 + 3 + 2 \quad \text{Consistent}$$
$$6 < 5 + 3 \qquad \text{Inconsistent}$$
$$5 < 3 + 2 \qquad \text{Inconsistent.}$$

We adjust the numbers, starting from the last inequality, always maintaining the initial order. We
change O_2 to 4 and O_1 to 8, to give the following
consistent set of equations:

$$8 < 4 + 3 + 2$$
$$8 > 4 + 3$$
$$4 < 3 + 2.$$

The relative value of each of the four objects has
now been obtained. We change it in this manner to
keep as close as possible to the original estimates
made by the individual. In case of equality in utility, appropriate equal signs are introduced.

APPENDIX **B** AN UNBIASED
ESTIMATE OF
THE LEVEL OF
SATISFACTION

    This section will prove that if one uses a
standard saturation level, then there exists an unbiased estimate of the level of satisfaction. This
proof holds if we consider the number of units needed to saturate and the number of units possessed as
continuous variables. It will be approximately true
in the case where they are discrete. Let x_i be the
number of units of an object which saturates the ith
individual. Let s_i be the number of units the ith
individual possesses.

Further, let $\quad x_i \sim f(x) \; ; \; x > 0$

and let $\quad s_i \sim h(s) \; ; \; 0 \leq s \leq x$

and $\quad x, s \sim p(s, x).$

The level of satisfaction n is defined as $\frac{s}{x}$. The
average level of satisfaction for a group of size N,
$\bar{n}$, is

$$\bar{n} = \frac{1}{N} \sum_{i=1}^{N} n_i = \int_{x=0}^{\infty} \int_{s=0}^{x} \frac{s}{x} p(s, x) \; ds \; dx.$$

The estimator $\hat{\bar{n}}$ is equal to

$$\hat{\bar{n}} = \frac{s}{X}; \; s \leq X$$

$$= 1; \; s > X,$$

where X is the standard saturation level. The expected value of $\hat{n}$ is then defined as

$$E(\hat{n}) = \int_{s=0}^{X} \frac{s}{X} h(s) \, ds = \int_{x=0}^{\infty} \int_{s=X}^{x} 1 \, p(s,x) \, ds \, dx$$

$$= \frac{1}{X} \int_{s=0}^{X} s \, h(s) \, ds + \int_{x=0}^{\infty} \int_{s=X}^{x} p(s,x) \, ds \, dx.$$

We wish to show that there exists an X such that
$E(\hat{n}) = \bar{n}$; that is, that for some X,

$$\frac{1}{X} \int_{s=0}^{X} s \, h(s) \, ds + \int_{x=0}^{\infty} \int_{s=X}^{x} p(s,x) \, ds \, dx$$

$$= \int_{x=0}^{\infty} \int_{s=0}^{x} \frac{s}{X} \, p(s,x) \, ds \, dx$$

or $A(X) = B(X) = \bar{n}.$

As $X \rightarrow 0$, $A(X)$ remains positive and $B(X) \rightarrow 1$, so
that $A(0) + B(0) > \bar{n}$, since $\bar{n}$ could never be greater
than 1. Furthermore, as $X \rightarrow \infty$ $A(X) \rightarrow 0$ and $B(X) \rightarrow 0$,
so that $A(\infty) + B(\infty) < \bar{n}$. Since the function
$A(X) + B(X)$ is a continuous, monotonic function of X,
it follows that there exists a value of X, say X_0,
for which $A(X_0) = B(X_0) = \bar{n}.$

Note that in the discrete case, this proof does
not hold because the function $A(X) + B(X)$ is discrete
function and must be written with integral signs
replaced by sums.

C

EXCERPTS FROM THE
QUESTIONNAIRE OF
THE PHILADELPHIA
WELFARE STUDY

The following sections are taken from the questionnaire prepared by J. Jahn and B. Gelin. Only those questions applicable to this study are presented. After each excerpt of the questions, we assign weights to the answers that correspond to the significance of the answers for our analysis in Chapter 6.

PART 1. COMPOSITION OF OBJECTS FOR INDIVIDUALISTIC FUNCTION

Household Possessions

1. During the past month, which of the following facilities did you own, have, or have access to in your building?

Ask	Check in appropriate column				
	Own (1)	Has (2)	Has Access (3)	No (4)	Other (specify) (5)
Elevator					
Central Heat					
Laundry Machine					
Cooking Stove (including hot plate)					
Refrigerator					

2. Does your home have a secure lock?

        (0)_____ Not applicable
        (1)_____ Yes
        (2)_____ No
        (x)_____ Don't know
        (y)_____ Other (specify) _____

3. Do you have a dining room table?

        (0)_____ Not applicable
        (1)_____ Yes
        (2)_____ No
        (x)_____ Don't know
        (y)_____ Other (specify) _____

4. Do you have your own bed? (Include bed shared
    with spouse; check (2) if shared with others, or
    if mattress without bed.)

        (0)_____ Not applicable
        (1)_____ Yes
        (2)_____ No
        (x)_____ Don't know
        (y)_____ Other (specify) _____

5. During the past six months, were your arrange-
    ments for

Ask	Check in appropriate column					
	Very satis-fac-tory	Satis-fac-tory	Nei-ther	Unsat-isfac-tory	Very unsat-isfac-tory	Other (spe-cify)
	(1)	(2)	(3)	(4)	(5)	(6)
House-cleaning	_____					
Shopping	_____					
Laundry	_____					
Repairs & Mainten-ance	_____					
Garbage Disposal	_____					

The set of units comprising the object "household possessions" totals 13. Answers are coded as
follows:

1. (5 units) Possession is signified by the
               answer "own," "have," or "have
               access to."

2.
3. } (3 units) Possession is signified by "yes."
4.

5. (5 units) Possession is signified by the
               answer "very satisfactory,"
               "satisfactory," or "neither."

Health

1. Do you need, own, or   Is it satisfactory, un-
    use any of the   satisfactory, or neither?
    following?

	Check in appropriate column			Check in appropriate column		
	Need (1)	Own (2)	Use (3)	Satis-factory (4)	Unsatis-factory (5)	Nei-ther (6)
Eyeglasses						
Hearing aid						
Cane						
Crutches						
Leg braces						
Special shoes						
Artificial limbs						
Dentures						

2a. During the past six months, were you sick at any time?

     <u>Check</u>

     (0)_____Not applicable
     (1)_____Yes
     (2)_____No
     (x)_____Don't know
     (y)_____Other (specify)_____

b. During the past six months, did you have any accidents, injuries, or poisonings?

     <u>Check</u>

     (0)_____Not applicable
     (1)_____Yes
     (2)_____No
     (x)_____Don't know
     (y)_____Other (specify)_____

c. During the past six months, did you have any other physical impairments or handicapping conditions, even though they did not interfere with your usual activities?

     <u>Check</u>

     (0)_____Not applicable
     (1)_____Yes
     (2)_____No
     (x)_____Don't know
     (y)_____Other (specify)_____

d. During the past six months, on about how many days were you ill?

     Ask and record number of days.

     _____Kept in bed all or most of the day/days because of any health condition?

3. During the past six months, did you see a physician or dentist about any illness or other

condition, in your house, in his office, or in a clinic?

Check

(0)_____Not applicable
(1)_____Yes
(2)_____No
(x)_____Don't know
(y)_____Other (specify)_____

4. Would you have liked to see a physician or dentist?

Check

(0)_____Not applicable
(1)_____Yes
(2)_____No
(x)_____Don't know
(y)_____Other (specify)_____

5. Did you see anyone else (e.g., chiropractor, spiritualist, etc.) for treatment of any illness or other condition during the past six months?

Check

(0)_____Not applicable
(1)_____Yes
(2)_____No
(x)_____Don't know
(y)_____Other (specify)_____

6. During the past six months, did you see a physician for a health examination or checkup not connected with a specific illness or condition?

Check

(0)_____Not applicable
(1)_____Yes
(2)_____No
(x)_____Don't know
(y)_____Other (specify)_____

7. Do you have a plan to see a doctor at regular
    times for a health examination or checkup, even
    when you are not feeling ill?

        Check

        (0)_____Not applicable
        (1)_____Yes
        (2)_____No
        (x)_____Don't know
        (y)_____Other (specify)_____

8. Do you have a plan to see a dentist at regular
    times for a dental checkup or examination?

        Check

        (0)_____Not applicable
        (1)_____Yes
        (2)_____No
        (x)_____Don't know
        (y)_____Other (specify)_____

9. During the past six months, were you cared for
    in a hospital, nursing home, or like institution,
    for an illness or health condition?

        Check

        (0)_____Not applicable
        (1)_____Yes
        (2)_____No
        (x)_____Don't know
        (y)_____Other (specify)_____

10. Read: Here is a series of questions concerning
           various health conditions. Tell me if any
           of these conditions have bothered you dur-
           ing the past six months and, if so, whether
           only a few times or often.

	Check in appropriate column		
	No	A few times	Often	Other
	(1)	(2)	(3)	(y)
Were you bothered by nervousness?				

	Check in appropriate column		
No (1)	A few times (2)	Often (3)	Other (y)

Were you bothered by your heart beating hard?

_____

Did you have spells of dizziness?

_____

Were you troubled by sick headaches?

_____

Were you bothered by having an upset stomach?

_____

Did you get up tired and exhausted in the mornings?

_____

Did you have a poor appetite?

_____

Were you bothered by not being able to go to the toilet regularly?

_____

Were you bothered by having to go to the toilet too frequently?

_____

Did you have any difficulties in sleeping?

_____

Did your health worry you?

_____

Did you find yourself having thoughts about death?

_____

Did you tire more easily than you used to a year ago?

_____

	Check in appropriate column			
	No (1)	A few times (2)	Often (3)	Other (y)
Were you bothered by not being able to remember things as well as you used to a year ago?				

The number of units comprising the object "health" totals 33. They are coded as follows:

1. (8 units) Possession is indicated by either "no need" or "need" and "satis-factory."

2. (4 units) Possession is indicated by "no."

3. (1 unit)   Possession is indicated by "yes."

4. (1 unit)   Possession is indicated by "no."

5. (1 unit)   Possession is indicated by "yes."

6.
7. } (3 units) Possession is indicated by "yes."
8.

9. (1 unit)   Possession is indicated by "no."

10. (14 units) Possession is indicated by "no."

Self-Image

1. In general, do you feel that you handle your own personal problems better than, as well as, or not as well as other people handle theirs?

        Check

        (0)_____Not applicable
        (1)_____Better
        (2)_____As well as
        (3)_____Not as well as
        (x)_____Don't know
        (y)_____Other (specify)_____

2.   In general, do other people feel you handle
     your own personal problems better than, as well
     as, or not as well as other people handle
     theirs?

          Check

          (0)_____Not applicable
          (1)_____Better
          (2)_____As well as
          (3)_____Not as well as
          (x)_____Don't know
          (y)_____Other (specify)_____

3.   During the past six months, have any particular
     changes or experiences occurred in your life that
     were upsetting and difficult to overcome or get
     used to?

          Check

          (0)_____Not applicable
          (1)_____Yes
          (2)_____No
          (x)_____Don't know
          (y)_____Other (specify)_____

4.   During the past months, was your life usually

          Ask

          (0)_____Not applicable
          (1)_____Very happy
          (2)_____Fairly happy
          (3)_____Neither
          (4)_____Fairly unhappy
          (5)_____Very unhappy
          (x)_____Don't know
          (y)_____Other (specify

5.   During the past months, how often did you feel
     that most of the time you spent during a day was
     useful to yourself or others?

Ask

(0)_____Not applicable
(1)_____Almost every day
(2)_____Most days
(3)_____Some days
(4)_____Almost no days
(5)_____No days
(x)_____Don't know
(y)_____Other (specify)_____

6. During the past months, was the value of what
    you did appreciated by other persons?

Ask

(0)_____Not applicable
(1)_____Almost always
(2)_____Usually
(3)_____Sometimes
(4)_____Hardly ever
(5)_____Never
(x)_____Don't know
(y)_____Other (specify)_____

7. During the past months, were you satisfied with
    the decisions which you made?

Ask

(0)_____Not applicable
(1)_____Almost always
(2)_____Usually
(3)_____Sometimes
(4)_____Hardly ever
(5)_____Never
(x)_____Don't know
(x)_____Other (specify)_____

8a. During the past months, as compared with a year
    ago, how easy or hard was it for you?

Ask

(0)_____Not applicable

(1)_____Much easier
(2)_____Somewhat easier
(3)_____About the same
(4)_____Somewhat harder
(5)_____Much harder
(x)_____Don't know
(y)_____Other (specify)_____

b. To work in or about your home?

     <u>Ask</u>

(0)_____Not applicable
(1)_____Much easier
(2)_____Somewhat easier
(3)_____About the same
(4)_____Somewhat harder
(5)_____Much harder
(x)_____Don't know
(y)_____Other (specify)_____

c. To make important decisions?

     <u>Ask</u>

(0)_____Not applicable
(1)_____Much easier
(2)_____Somewhat easier
(3)_____About the same
(4)_____Somewhat harder
(5)_____Much harder
(x)_____Don't know
(y)_____Other (specify)_____

d. To make plans for the future?

     <u>Ask</u>

(0)_____Not applicable
(1)_____Much easier
(2)_____Somewhat easier
(3)_____About the same
(4)_____Somewhat harder
(5)_____Much harder
(x)_____Don't know
(y)_____Other (specify)_____

e. To maintain your personal appearance?

Ask

(0)_____Not applicable
(1)_____Much easier
(2)_____Somewhat easier
(3)_____About the same
(4)_____Somewhat harder
(5)_____Much harder
(x)_____Don't know
(y)_____Other (specify)_____

f. To make friends?

Ask

(0)_____Not applicable
(1)_____Much easier
(2)_____Somewhat easier
(3)_____About the same
(4)_____Somewhat harder
(5)_____Much harder
(x)_____Don't know
(y)_____Other (specify)_____

9. These are opinions that have been expressed by
    various people. To what extent would you agree
    or disagree? There are no right or wrong
    answers.

a. Things will get better only if you get out and
    do something to make them better.

Ask

(0)_____Not applicable
(1)_____Strongly agree
(2)_____Agree
(3)_____Neither
(4)_____Disagree
(5)_____Strongly disagree
(x)_____Don't know
(y)_____Other (specify)_____

b. Anyone with ability and willingness to work has
    a good chance of being successful.

        Ask

        (0)_____Not applicable
        (1)_____Strongly agree
        (2)_____Agree
        (3)_____Neither
        (4)_____Disagree
        (5)_____Strongly disagree
        (x)_____Don't know
        (y)_____Other (specify)_____

c. No one cares much what happens to you.

        Ask

        (0)_____Not applicable
        (1)_____Strongly agree
        (2)_____Agree
        (3)_____Neither
        (4)_____Disagree
        (5)_____Strongly disagree
        (x)_____Don't know
        (y)_____Other (specify)_____

d. Real friends are easy to find.

        Ask

        (0)_____Not applicable
        (1)_____Strongly agree
        (2)_____Agree
        (3)_____Neither
        (4)_____Disagree
        (5)_____Strongly disagree
        (x)_____Don't know
        (y)_____Other (specify)_____

e. Most people can be trusted.

        Ask

        (0)_____Not applicable

(1)_____Strongly agree
(2)_____Agree
(3)_____Neither
(4)_____Disagree
(5)_____Strongly disagree
(x)_____Don't know
(y)_____Other (specify)_____

f. There is really no point in living.

   <u>Ask</u>

(0)_____Not applicable
(1)_____Strongly agree
(2)_____Agree
(3)_____Neither
(4)_____Disagree
(5)_____Strongly disagree
(x)_____Don't know
(y)_____Other (specify)_____

g. It is great to be living in these exciting times.

   <u>Ask</u>

(0)_____Not applicable
(1)_____Strongly agree
(2)_____Agree
(3)_____Neither
(4)_____Disagree
(5)_____Strongly disagree
(x)_____Don't know
(y)_____Other (specify)_____

Self-image is composed of 20 units. The following answers denote possession.

1.⎫ (2 units) Possession is denoted by "better
2.⎭   than" or "as well as."

3. (1 unit)   Possession is signified by "no."

4. (1 unit)   Possession is signified by "very
               happy," "fairly happy," or
               "neither."

5. (1 unit) Possession is indicated by "almost every day," "most days," or "some days."

6. ⎫
7. ⎬ (2 units) Possession is indicated by "almost always," "usually" or "sometimes."
   ⎭

8. (6 units) Possession is indicated by "much easier," "somewhat easier" or "about the same."

9. (7 units) Possession is indicated by "strongly agree," "agree," or "neither" for units a,b,d,e, and g by "disagree" or "strongly disagree" for c and f.

Inter-Personal Relations

1. During the past month, how did you get along with your neighbors or persons living near your place of residence? Were you

        Ask

        (0)_____Not applicable
        (1)_____Friendly to all
        (2)_____Friendly to most
        (3)_____Friendly to some
        (4)_____Friendly to none
        (x)_____Don't know
        (y)_____Other (specify)_____

2. During the past month, as compared to a year ago, did you have more or fewer close friends?

        Ask

        (0)_____Not applicable
        (1)_____Many more
        (2)_____Some more
        (3)_____About the same
        (4)_____Some fewer
        (5)_____Many fewer

(x)_____Don't know
(y)_____Other (specify)

3. During the past month, did you spend time with one or more friends or neighbors in social or recreational activities?

    Ask

    (0)_____Not applicable
    (1)_____Almost every day
    (2)_____Most days
    (3)_____About once a week
    (4)_____A few days
    (5)_____No days
    (x)_____Don't know
    (y)_____Other (specify)_____

4. During the past month, did you visit, telephone or write letters to persons other than relatives or members of the household?

    Ask

    (0)_____Not applicable
    (1)_____Almost every day
    (2)_____Most days
    (3)_____About once a week
    (4)_____A few days
    (5)_____No days
    (x)_____Don't know
    (y)_____Other (specify)_____

5. During the past month, did you give personal help or services to one or more friends or neighbors?

    Ask

    (0)_____Not applicable
    (1)_____Almost every day
    (2)_____Most days
    (3)_____About once a week
    (4)_____A few days
    (5)_____No days

(x)_____Don't know
(y)_____Other (specify)_____

6. During the past month, did you receive any per-
    sonal help or service, from one or more friends
    or neighbors?

        Ask

    (0)_____Not applicable
    (1)_____Almost every day
    (2)_____Most days
    (3)_____About once a week
    (4)_____A few days
    (5)_____No days
    (x)_____Don't know
    (y)_____Other (specify)_____

7. During the past month, did you see or hear from
    one or more of these relatives, including by phone
    or letters?

        Ask

    (0)_____Not applicable
    (1)_____Almost every day
    (2)_____Most days
    (3)_____About once a week
    (4)_____A few days
    (5)_____No days
    (x)_____Don't know
    (y)_____Other (specify)_____

8. During the past month, did you visit one or more
    of these relatives?

        Ask

    (0)_____Not applicable
    (1)_____Almost every day
    (2)_____Most days
    (3)_____About once a week
    (4)_____A few days
    (5)_____No days
    (x)_____Don't know
    (y)_____Other (specify) _____

9. During the past month, did you give any personal help or services to one or more of these relatives?

Ask

(0)_____Not applicable
(1)_____Almost every day
(2)_____Most days
(3)_____About once a week
(4)_____A few days
(5)_____No days
(x)_____Don't know
(y)_____Other (specify)_____

10. During the past month, did you receive any personal help or services from one or more of these relatives?

Ask

(0)_____Not applicable
(1)_____Almost every day
(2)_____Most days
(3)_____About once a week
(4)_____A few days
(5)_____No days
(x)_____Don't know
(y)_____Other (specify)_____

11. During the past month, has your married life usually been

Ask

(0)_____Not applicable
(1)_____Very happy
(2)_____Happy
(3)_____Neither happy nor unhappy
(4)_____Sometimes happy, sometimes unhappy
(5)_____Unhappy
(x)_____Don't know
(y)_____Other (specify)_____

12. Would you say that during this past month, as compared to a year ago, your married life has been

Ask

```
(0)_____Not applicable
(1)_____Much happier
(2)_____Somewhat happier
(3)_____About the same
(4)_____Somewhat unhappier
(5)_____Much unhappier
(x)_____Don't know
(y)_____Other (specify)_____
```

13. In general, during the past month, as compared
    with most other couples you know of, do you
    think that you and your (Husband/Wife) got along

    Ask

```
(0)_____Not applicable
(1)_____Better
(2)_____As well
(3)_____Not as well
(x)_____Don't know
(y)_____Other (specify)_____
```

14. During the past month, did you spend time
    doing things for persons in the household?

    Ask

```
(0)_____Not applicable
(1)_____Almost every day
(2)_____Most days
(3)_____About once a week
(4)_____A few days
(5)_____No days
(x)_____Don't know
(y)_____Other (specify)_____
```

15. During the past month, did others in the house-
    hold spend time doing things for you?

    Ask

```
(0)_____Not applicable
(1)_____Almost every day
(2)_____Most days
```

(3)_____About once a week
(4)_____A few days
(5)_____No days
(x)_____Don't know
(y)_____Other (specify)_____

16. During the past month, has your relationship to
     other persons living in the household been:

          Ask

          (0)_____Not applicable
          (1)_____Very happy
          (2)_____Happy
          (3)_____Neither happy nor unhappy
          (4)_____Sometimes happy, sometimes unhappy
          (5)_____Unhappy
          (6)_____Very unhappy
          (x)_____Don't know
          (y)_____Other (specify)_____

     Inter-personal relations consists of 16 units
for married people and 13 for non-married adults and
children. The answers are coded in the following
manner.

     1.   (1 unit)   Possession denoted by "friendly
                     to all," "to most," or "to some."

     2.   (1 unit)   Possession denoted by "many
                     more," "some more," or "about
                     the same."

     3.
    thru (8 units) Possession denoted by "almost
     10.   every day," "most days," or
                     "about once a week."

     11. (1 unit)   Possession denoted by "very
                     happy," "happy," "neither happy
                     nor unhappy," or "sometimes
                     happy, sometimes unhappy."

     12. (1 unit)   Possession denoted by "much
                     happier," somewhat happier," or
                     about the same."

13.   (1 unit)   Possession denoted by "better"
                  or "as well."

14. ⎫ (2 units)   Possession denoted by "almost
15. ⎭   every day," "most days," or
                  "about once a week."

16.   (1 unit)   Possession denoted by "very
                  happy," "happy," "neither happy
                  nor unhappy," or "sometimes
                  happy, sometimes unhappy."

PART 2.   THE RELATIVE IMPORTANCE OF A NEED

The relative importance of these objects is obtained as follows: From the following rating schedule a value is obtained for self-image from self-
acceptance and self-responsibility, for health from
physical and emotional health, for interpersonal
relations from effectiveness in social living, and
housing from material circumstances. This paper was
filled out only when the participant was interviewed
directly.

Movement and Component Factors Rating Schedule

Judge the adaptive status of the individual with respect to each of the component factors by means of the following rating scale. Insert your ratings of status in the column to the right of each factor.

L	SCALE OF ADAPTIVE AND ADJUSTIVE STATUS	H
O		I
W	1 2 3 4 5 6 7 8 9 10 11	G
	Very Poor Average Good Excel-	H
	Poor lent	

12   Insufficient evidence
13   Not relevant

AREA	COMPONENT FACTOR	STATUS
UNDER-STANDING	Understanding of reality	
	Self-Understanding	
ATTITUDES	Self-Acceptance	
	Self-Responsibility	
ADAPTIVE EFFICIENCY AND DIS-ABLING HABITS	Occupational Efficiency	
	Physical Health	
	Emotional Health	
	Effectiveness in Social Living	
	(1) Within Family	
	(2) Outside Family	
ENVIRON-MENTAL CIRCUM-STANCES	Social Environment	
	(1) Within Family	
	(2) Outside Family	
	Material Circumstances	

OVERALL LEVEL OF ADJUSTMENT AND ADAPTATION

Each of the values is subtracted from 12 and expressed as a percentage of their sum. The reason for this is that we are assuming the relative importance of an object to be inversely proportional to its relative present condition as measured by the interviewer's responses on the above rating schedule.

PART 3. DEFINITION OF MEASURES FOR SOCIETAL FUNCTION

Net Contribution to Gross National Product

The following questions were designed to determine the amount of income the individual earned and the amount of income, medical aid, and other aid he received. The individual's contribution to the gross national product will be determined by subtracting the aid he received from his earned income. The individual is first asked:

About how much was your total income during the last calendar year from all sources:

    a. $5,000 or over
    b. $4,000 to $4,999
    c. $3,000 to $3,999
    d. $2,000 to $2,999
    e. $1,000 to $1,999
    f. $ 500 to $ 999
    g. $ 0 to $ 499

The sources of the individual's income are classified in the following way:

    1.   Income from employment
    2.   Social Security
    3.   Public assistance
    4.   Unemployment insurance
    5.   Veteran's compensation and pensions
    6.   Other pensions, annuities, settlements,
            or payments
    7.   Interest, dividends, and rentals
    8.   Gifts or contributions
    9.   Support of dependents from OASDI
   10.   Support of dependents from public assistance.

The individual is then asked how much of his income comes from each of the above sources.

Sources 1, 2, 6 and 7 are considered positive contributions.

Crime Rate

The individual is questioned as to his relationship with the police, and his arrest and conviction record. From this his crimes will be classified by type (using the Federal Bureau of Investigation's definitions) into index crimes and other crimes. Obviously only reported crimes are available; but using calculations made by the President's Commission on Crime (1966), one can estimate the number of unreported crimes.

Level of Education

The individual is asked the extent of his formal education, the years of school completed, the degrees and diplomas received. The highest level attained is used as a measure.

Religious and Community Participation

The extent and scope of the individual's participation in religious and community organizations is determined by asking the following questions:

1. During the past six months, did you belong to or take part in activities of any groups or organizations in the community? Which ones?

2. For each of those listed above

    a. Did you attend meetings?
    b. Were you a member?
    c. Did you do work?
    d. Were you an officer?
    e. Did you contribute?

3. During the past month, how much time did
you spend in activities of these groups or organizations?

      a. Most days
      b. 2-3 days per week
      c. About once a week
      d. 10 days

4. During the past month, did you, as a member
of a social group or organization, without being
paid, give help or services to other people?

      a. Most days
      b. 2-3 days per week
      c. About once a week
      d. 10 days

5. During the past year, did you vote in a
national, state, or local election?

The extent of the individual's participation
will be represented by the total number of points he
received for his responses. Points are assigned as
follows:

2 a	2	points
2 b	1	point
2 c	4	points
2 d	5	points
2 e	3	points
3 a	10	points
3 b	8	points
3 c	4	points
3 d	2	points
4 a	10	points
4 b	8	points
4 c	4	points
4 d	2	points
5	5	points

Level of Information

A list of 27 activities, encompassing both those
in which information can be transmitted and those in

which information cannot be transmitted, was prepared.
The individual was asked to indicate which ones he
engaged in during his spare time. Those activities
which are starred in the following list are considered as contributing to the individual's level of
information.

   1. Nap and rest
   2. Sit and think
   3. Sit and watch activity of others
 *4. Listen to radio
 *5. Watch television
 *6. Read
   7. Sew, crochet, knit
 *8. Write letters
 *9. Write books, articles, etc.
10. Paint, draw
11. Do shop work
12. Play musical instrument
13. Work in and around house
*14. Talk on telephone
*15. Go to movies
*16. Go to theater, concert, etc.
*17. Go to library
18. Take a ride
19. Go for a walk
20. Go shopping
21. Play outdoor sports
*22. Go to evening school
*23. Go to church
24. Play cards or other table games
25. Visit or entertain friends of relatives
*26. Attend meeting of club, lodge, etc.
*27. Participate in community activities

The individual's level of information will be
represented by the total number of affirmative
answers to the starred items.

APPENDIX D COMPUTATION OF WEIGHTED
LEVELS OF SATISFACTION,
USING THE PROCEDURES
DEVELOPED IN CHAPTER 3

Since the data for all strata given in Table 1 are voluminous, we present here only the detailed computations for one stratum, B1 (current clients of standard service), which adequately demonstrate the procedures.

Housing

Levels of Satisfaction	Relative Importance	Weighted Levels of Satisfaction
.83	.35	.29
.75	.34	.26
.75	.20	.15
.80	.25	.20
.75	.36	.27
.83	.33	.27
.83	.37	.31
.75	.29	.22
.83	.33	.27

Self-Image

Levels of Satisfaction	Relative Importance	Weighted Levels of Satisfaction
.95	.24	.23
.90	.23	.18
.45	.25	.11
.75	.25	.18
.85	.26	.22
.70	.31	.22
.75	.20	.15
.75	.31	.23
.75	.26	.20

Health

Levels of Satisfaction	Relative Importance	Weighted Levels of Satisfaction
.48	.21	.10
.58	.17	.10
.45	.30	.14
.82	.21	.17
.73	.16	.12
.70	.18	.13
.70	.19	.13
.94	.18	.17
.82	.18	.15

Inter-personal Relations

Levels of Satisfaction	Relative Importance	Weighted Levels of Satisfaction
.75	.20	.15
.54	.26	.14
.38	.25	.10
.31	.24	.07
.31	.26	.08
.56	.26	.15
.55	.25	.14
1.00	.24	.24
.69	.22	.15
.46	.23	.11

APPENDIX TABLE 1

Representative Summaries of Weighted Levels for All Needs

| | | Individual Weighted Level for Each Need | | | Total Level of Satisfaction |
Adults	I.P.R.	Health	Housing	S.I.	
1	.15	.10	.29	.23	.77
9	.14	.10	.26	.18	.68
11	.10	.14	.15	.11	.50
13	.07	.17	.20	.18	.62
17	.08	.12	.27	.22	.69
21	.15	.13	.27	.22	.77
Children					
1	.24	.13	.31	.15	.83
9	.15	.17	.22	.23	.77
17	.11	.15	.27	.20	.73

APPENDIX   E   ILLUSTRATION OF A
                 PROGRAM'S CHANGE IN
                 VALUE WHEN DISTRIBUTION
                 OF INDIVIDUAL UTILITIES
                 IS CONSIDERED, USING
                 ALTERNATIVE FAIRNESS
                 FUNCTIONS

APPENDIX FIGURE 1

Diagram of Relative Loss or Gain in Utility
for Five Alternative Fairness Functions

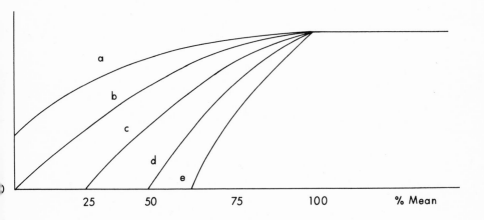

KEY

Function Value

% of Mean	a	b	c	d	e
100 & over	1.00	1.00	1.00	1.00	1.00
90	1.00	1.00	0.98	0.95	0.90
80	0.98	0.96	0.91	0.85	0.70
70	0.95	0.90	0.83	0.70	0.50
60	0.92	0.85	0.72	0.53	0.15
50	0.88	0.78	0.60	0.30	0.00
40	0.80	0.69	0.43	0.03	0.00
30	0.75	0.58	0.22	0.00	0.00
20	0.65	0.42	0.00	0.00	0.00
10	0.55	0.22	0.00	0.00	0.00
0	0.40	0.00	0.00	0.00	0.00

Effect of the Fairness Function on the
Results Presented in Chapter 6

Adults

Stratum	Unweighted	Function				
		a	b	c	d	e
A1	18	17	17	16	16	15
A2	7	7	7	7	7	6
B1	11	11	11	11	11	11
B2	5	5	5	5	5	5
B3	7	7	7	7	6	6
B4	7	7	7	7	7	6
B5	14	10	10	10	9	9

Children

Stratum	Unweighted	Function				
		a	b	c	d	e
A1	15	15	14	14	13	12
A2	11	10	10	10	10	9
B1	25	25	24	24	22	21
B2	--	--	--	--	--	--
B3	12	12	12	12	12	11
B4	--	--	--	--	--	--
B5	12	11	11	11	10	10

APPENDIX TABLE 3

Sample Computations for Stratum B1 to Obtain the Effect of the Fairness
Function on the Results Presented in Chapter 6

Adults	% of Mean	Fairness Function Value				
		a	b	c	d	e
31	100+	1.00	1.00	1.00	1.00	1.00
1	9	0.50	0.20	0.00	0.00	0.00
10	88	1.00	0.99	0.97	0.94	0.88
0	0	0.40	0.00	0.00	0.00	0.00
14	100+	1.00	1.00	1.00	1.00	1.00
12	100+	1.00	1.00	1.00	1.00	1.00
average (11)		11	11	11	11	11
Children						
28	100+	1.00	1.00	1.00	1.00	1.00
36	100+	1.00	1.00	1.00	1.00	1.00
11	53	0.88	0.78	0.60	0.30	0.00
average (25)		25	24	24	22	21

BIBLIOGRAPHY

BIBLIOGRAPHY

Ackoff, R. L. _Scientific Method_. New York: J. Wiley and Sons, 1962.

Advisory Commission of Intergovernmental Relations. _Performance of Urban Functions, Local and Areawide_. 1963.

_____. _Metropolitan Social and Economic Disparities--Implications for Intergovernmental Relations in Central Cities and Suburbs_. 1965.

Alberts, D. S. "The Application of the Cost-Performance Analysis to the Evaluation of Distribution Systems." Master's thesis, University of Pennsylvania, 1966.

_____. "Students' Perceptions of Their Professors." Unpublished, 1966.

Arrow, K. _Social Choice and Individual Values_. New York: J. Wiley and Sons, 1951.

Banfield, E. C., and Meyerson, M. "Notes on a Conceptual Scheme." _Politics, Planning and the Public Interest_. Glencoe, Illinois: Free Press of Glencoe, 1955.

Bauer, R. A. _Social Indicators_. Cambridge, Massachusetts: MIT Press, 1966.

Baumol, W. J. "Community Indifference." _The Review of Economic Studies_ (1946-47).

Bell, D. "Toward a Communal Society," _Life_, LXII, 19 (May, 1967).

Bergson, A. "A Reformulation of Certain Aspects of
    Welfare Economics," _Quarterly Journal of Eco-
    nomics_, LII (February, 1938).

Biderman, A. D. "Social Indicators and Goals."
    Social Indicators (Cambridge, Massachusetts:
    MIT Press, 1966.

Burtt, E. A., ed. _The English Philosophers from
    Bacon to Mill_. New York: Random House, 1939.

Calder, N. _The World in 1984_. Volume 1. New York:
    Penguin Books, 1964.

Chapin, F. S. _Experimental Design in Sociological
    Research_. New York: Harper & Brothers, 1955.

Churchman, C. W. _Prediction and Optimal Decision_.
    Englewood Cliffs, New Jersey: Prentice-Hall,
    Inc., 1961.

City of Philadelphia. _Annual Report--Department of
    Public Welfare_. 1965.

Cochran, W. G. _Sampling Techniques_. New York: J.
    Wiley and Sons, 1953.

Cornford, F. M., trans. _The Republic of Plato_.
    New York: Oxford University Press, 1958.
    (First Edition, 15th Printing.)

Croxton, F. E., and Cowden, D. J. _Applied General
    Statistics_. Englewood Cliffs, New Jersey:
    Prentice-Hall, Inc., 1955.

Cumming, R. D. _The Philosophy of Jean Paul Sartre_.
    New York: Random House, 1965.

Desan, W. _The Marxism of Jean Paul Sartre_. New
    York: Doubleday, 1965.

Edgeworth, F. Y. _Mathematical Psychics_. London:
    Kegan Paul and Company, 1881.

Ellis, H. S. A Survey of Contemporary Economics.
    Philadelphia: The Blakiston Company, 1948.

Gorham, W. "Allocating Federal Resources Among
    Competing Social Needs," Indicators (August,
    1966).

Gross, B. M. The State of the Nation. London:
    Tavistock, 1966.

Hansen, M. A., Hurwitz, W. N., and Madow, W. A.
    Sample Survey Methods and Theory. New York:
    J. Wiley and Sons, 1953.

Hegel, G. Philosophy of Right. Oxford: Clarendon
    Press, 1942.

Hicks, J. R. "The Foundations of Welfare Economics,"
    Economic Journal, XLIX (December, 1939).

_____. "The Rehabilitation of Consumer's Surplus,"
    The Review of Economic Studies, VIII, 2 (1941).

_____, Hart, A. G., and Ford, J. W. The Social
    Framework of the American Economy. New York:
    Oxford University Press, 1955.

Hildreth, C. "Alternative Conditions for Social
    Orderings," Econometrica, XXI (1953).

Hill, J. G. "Cost Analysis of Social Work Service."
    Social Work Research. Chicago: University of
    Chicago Press, 1960.

Hook, S. Political Power and Personal Freedom.
    New York: Criterion Books, 1959.

Jahn, J. "The Statistical Definition of Predicted
    Measures of Effectiveness of Alternative
    Programs of Health, Education and Welfare."
    Philadelphia: School of Social Work,
    University of Pennsylvania, 1965. Mimeo-
    graphed.

_____. "The Utilization, Cost and Effectiveness of 'Anti-Poverty' Programs." Philadelphia: School of Social Work, University of Pennsylvania, 1965. Mimeographed.

_____. "General Methods and Conditions for the Selection of 'Criterion Variables' to Measure Effectiveness of Welfare Programs." Philadelphia: School of Social Work, University of Pennsylvania, 1966. Mimeographed.

_____, and Blenker, M. Serving the Aging, Methodological Supplement--Part 1--Experimental Design and Statistical Tests of Hypotheses. New York: Community Service Society of New York, 1964.

_____, and Gelin, B. A. Philadelphia Child Welfare Project: Research Design for Phase I, 1965-66. Philadelphia: Research Center, School of Social Work, University of Pennsylvania, 1966.

_____, and Lewis, H. "An Experiment to Measure and Optimize the Utilization, Cost and Effectiveness of Child Welfare Programs." Philadelphia: School of Social Work, University of Pennsylvania, 1966. Mimeographed.

Kaldor, N. "Welfare Propositions of Economics and Interpersonal Comparisons of Utility," Economic Journal, XLIX (September, 1939).

Kant, I. "Foundations of the Metaphysics of Morals." Critique of Practical Reason and Other Writings in Moral Philosophy. Chicago: University of Chicago Press, 1949.

Kaplan, A. The New World of Philosophy. New York: Random House, 1961.

Kempthorne, O. The Design and Analysis of Experiments. New York: J. Wiley and Sons, 1952.

Kendrick, J. W. Productivity Trends in the United States. Princeton, New Jersey: Princeton University Press, 1961.

Kogan, L. S., and Shyne, A. W. "Tender-Minded and
    Tough-Minded Approaches in Evaluative Research,"
    Welfare in Review, IV, 2 (February, 1966).

Lange, O. "The Foundations of Welfare Economics,"
    Econometrica, X (1942).

Laski, H. J. Karl Marx--An Essay. New York: League
    for Industrial Democracy, 1925.

Lerner, A. P. Economics of Control. New York:
    Macmillan, 1944.

Levine, A. S. "Cost-Benefit Analysis of the Work
    Experience Program," Welfare in Review
    (September, 1966).

Levinson, P. "Evaluation of Social Welfare Programs--
    Two Research Models," Welfare in Review (March,
    1966).

Lewis, H., et al. Designing More Effective Protective
    Services. Philadelphia: Research Center, School
    of Social Work, University of Pennsylvania, 1967.

_____, and Bishop, J. A. "Plan for Alternative
    Services--Part I." Philadelphia: School of
    Social Work, University of Pennsylvania, 1966.
    Mimeographed.

_____, and Jahn, J. "Intervening in the Recurrence
    Cycle of Neglect and Abuse of Children After
    Protective Service." Philadelphia: School of
    Social Work, University of Pennsylvania, 1964.
    Mimeographed.

Little, I. M. D. "A Reformulation of the Theory of
    Consumers' Behavior," Oxford Economic Papers
    (January, 1965). (Second Edition.)

_____. A Critique of Welfare Economics. London:
    Oxford University Press, 1960.

Marx, K., and Engels, F. Manifesto of the Communist
    Party. New York: League for Industrial Democ-
    racy, 1925.

Meier, R. L. Science and Economic Development.
    Cambridge, Massachusetts: MIT Press, 1966.

Morgenstern, O. On the Accuracy of Economic Obser-
    vations. Princeton, New Jersey: Princeton
    University Press, 1950.

Nicol, H. O. "Guaranteed Income Maintenance--A
    Public Welfare Systems Model," Welfare in
    Review (November, 1966).

Office of Economic Opportunity. Community Action
    Program Guide. Volume I. Washington, D.C.:
    Government Printing Office, 1965.

_____. Catalog of Federal Programs for Individual
    and Community Improvement. Washington, D.C.:
    Government Printing Office, 1965.

Ornati, O. "Affluence and the Risk of Poverty,"
    Social Research, XXXI (1964).

Pigou, A. C. The Economics of Welfare. Fourth
    edition. London: Macmillan, 1952.

Polonsky, N. A. Social Work Research. Chicago:
    University of Chicago Press, 1960.

President's Commission on Law Enforcement and Adminis-
    tration of Justice. The Challenge of Crime in
    a Free Society. Washington, D.C.: Government
    Printing Office, 1967.

President's Commission on National Goals. Goals for
    Americans. Englewood Cliffs, New Jersey:
    Prentice-Hall, Inc., 1960.

President's Research Committee on Social Trends.
    Recent Social Trends in the United States.
    New York: McGraw-Hill, 1933.

Rapoport, A. Operational Philosophy. New York:
    J. Wiley and Sons, 1965.

Reder, M. W. Studies in the Theory of Welfare Economic
    New York: Columbia University Press, 1947.

Russell, B. A History of Western Philosophy. New
     York: Simon and Schuster, 1945.

Samuelson, P. A. Foundations of Economic Analysis.
     Cambridge, Massachusetts: Harvard University
     Press, 1947.

Sartre, J. Nausea. Norfolk, Connecticut: New
     Directions, 1959.

Schultz, H. The Theory and Measurement of Demand.
     Chicago: University of Chicago Press, 1938.

Scitovsky, T. "A Note on Welfare Propositions in
     Economics," The Review of Economic Studies,
     IX, 2 (1941).

_____, "A Reconsideration of the Theory of Tariffs,"
     ibid.

Singer, E. A. On the Contented Life. New York:
     H. Holt and Company, 1923.

_____. In Search of a Way of Life. New York:
     Columbia University Press, 1948.

Stevens, S. S. "A Metric for the Social Consensus,"
     Science, CLI (1966).

_____, and Galanter, E. H. "Ratio Scales and
     Category Scales for a Dozen Perceptual Continua,"
     Journal of Experimental Psychology, LIV.

Taylor, A. E. Aristotle. London: Dover, 1955.

The American Assembly. Goals for Americans.
     Englewood Cliffs, New Jersey: Prentice-Hall,
     Inc., 1964.

U.S. Department of Health, Education and Welfare.
     Handbook on Programs. Washington, D.C.:
     Government Printing Office, 1963.

White, H.C. "Cause and Effect in Social Mobility
     Tables." Behavioral Science, VIII (January, 1963).

Wolins, M. "Measuring the Effect of Social Work
     Intervention." Social Work Research. Chicago:
     University of Chicago Press, 1960.

Woodbridge, F. J. E., ed. Hobbes Selections. New
     York: Charles Scribner's Sons, 1958.

INDEX

INDEX

ABOUT THE AUTHOR

David S. Alberts is currently an Assistant Professor in the Department of Quantitative Analysis at New York University, where he specializes in operations research. He is also a coordinator of the Computer Science Program at NYU's School of Commerce. He has been teaching and developing courses in statistics, decision theory, management science, information systems, and the application of operations research methodology to urban and social problems.

Dr. Alberts has acted as a consultant to Flower and Fifth Avenue Hospital and Mount Sinai Hospital on computer applications and simulation models, and has helped to design experiments. He has developed and taught training courses for the Department of Civil Service of New York State and the American Telephone and Telegraph Company. Other consulting work has included the conceptualization and design of information systems for such corporations as CCM Information Sciences and Flying Mercury.

Dr. Alberts received his doctorate in operations research from the University of Pennsylvania.